CGP

GCSE AQA
Combined Science
Chemistry
Foundation Level

No doubt about it, the Chemistry part of GCSE Combined Science is tough. Not to worry — this CGP book has it covered, from facts and theory to practical skills.

What's more, each topic in this book includes exam-style practice, *and* we've put in a full set of Chemistry practice papers to help you sharpen up your exam skills.

How to access your free Online Edition

This book includes a free Online Edition to read on your PC, Mac or tablet. You'll just need to go to **cgpbooks.co.uk/extras** and enter this code:

4096 9659 4852 7936

By the way, this code only works for one person. If somebody else has used this book before you, they might have already claimed the Online Edition.

Complete
Revision & Practice
<u>Everything</u> you need to pass the exams!

Contents

Throughout this book you'll see grade stamps like these:

These grade stamps help to show how difficult the questions are.

Remember — to get a top grade you need to be able to answer **all** the questions, not just the hardest ones.

In the real exams, some questions test how well you can structure an answer (as well as your scientific knowledge). In this book, we've marked these questions with an asterisk (*).

Topic 4 — Chemical Changes

Topic 5 — Energy Changes

Topic 6 — The Rate and Extent of Chemical Change

Topic 7 — Organic Chemistry

Topic 8 — Chemical Analysis

Topic 9 — Chemistry of the Atmosphere

Topic 10 — Using Resources

Khawajamoon786.

Practical Skills

Practice Exams

Published by CGP

Editors: Alex Billings, Emma Clayton, Paul Jordin and Caroline Purvis.

Contributor: Paddy Gannon

From original material by Richard Parsons.

With thanks to Mary Falkner, Katherine Faudemer, Jamie Sinclair and Hayley Thompson for the proofreading.

With thanks to Emily Smith for the copyright research.

ISBN: 978 1 78908 003 2

Printed by Elanders Ltd, Newcastle upon Tyne.
Clipart from Corel®

What to Expect in the Exams

Before you get cracking with your <u>revision</u> and <u>exam practice</u>, here's a <u>handy guide</u> to what you'll have to face in the exams — and the <u>special features</u> of this book that we've included especially to <u>help you</u>. You're welcome.

1. Topics are Covered in Different Papers

For GCSE Combined Science, you'll sit <u>six exam papers</u> at the <u>end</u> of your course, including <u>two chemistry exams</u>.

Paper	Time	No. of marks	Topics Assessed
Chemistry 1	1 hr 15 mins	70	1, 2, 3, 4 and 5
Chemistry 2	1 hr 15 mins	70	6, 7, 8, 9 and 10

You're expected to know the basic concepts of chemistry in both chemistry papers.

2. There are Different Question Types

In each exam, you'll be expected to answer a mixture of <u>multiple choice</u> questions, <u>structured</u> questions, questions that have <u>short, closed answers</u>, as well as <u>open response</u> questions.

For some <u>open response</u> questions, you'll be marked on the <u>overall quality</u> of your answer, not just its <u>scientific content</u>. So...

Fortunately, we've included loads of <u>questions</u> in this book, as well as a <u>set of practice papers</u> to give you the <u>best possible preparation</u> for the exams.

<u>Always</u> make sure:
- You answer the question <u>fully</u>.
- You include <u>detailed, relevant information</u>.
- Your answer is <u>clear</u> and has a <u>logical structure</u>.

In the exam practice questions, we've marked these questions with an asterisk (*).

3. You'll be Tested on your Maths...

At least <u>20% of the total marks</u> for GCSE Combined Science will come from questions that test your <u>maths skills</u>. For these questions, always remember to:

EXAMPLE:

Look out for these <u>worked examples</u> in this book — they show you maths skills you'll need in the exam.

- Show your <u>working</u> — you could get marks for this, even if your final answer's wrong.
- Check that the <u>units</u> of your <u>answer</u> are the same as the ones they asked for in the question.
- Make sure your answer is given to an appropriate number of <u>significant figures</u>.

4. ...and on your Practical Skills

Whenever one of the <u>required practicals</u> crops up in this book, it's marked up with stamps like these...

...and there's a whole section on Practical Skills on pages 147-152.

- GCSE Combined Science contains <u>21 required practicals</u> that you'll do during the course. The <u>6 chemistry practicals</u> are covered in this book. You can be asked about these, and the practical skills involved in them, in the exams.
- At least <u>15% of the total marks</u> will be for questions that test your understanding of the practical activities and practical skills.
- For example, you might be asked to comment on the <u>design</u> of an experiment (the <u>apparatus</u> and <u>method</u>), make <u>predictions</u>, <u>analyse</u> or <u>interpret results</u>... Pretty much anything to do with planning and carrying out the investigations.

5. You'll need to know about Working Scientifically

<u>Working Scientifically</u> is all about how science is applied in the outside world by <u>real scientists</u>.

For example, you might be asked about ways that scientists <u>communicate</u> an idea to get their point across without being <u>biased</u>, or about the <u>limitations</u> of a scientific theory.

Working Scientifically is covered on pages 2-16.

You need to think about the <u>situation</u> that you've been given and use all your <u>scientific savvy</u> to answer the question. Always <u>read the question</u> and any <u>data</u> you've been given really carefully <u>before</u> you start writing your answer.

The Scientific Method

This section isn't about how to 'do' science — but it does show you the way most scientists work.

Science is All About Testing Hypotheses

Scientists make an observation

1) Scientists observe (look at) something they don't understand.
2) They come up with a possible explanation for what they've observed.
3) This explanation is called a hypothesis.

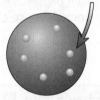

About 100 years ago, scientists thought that atoms looked like this.

They test their hypothesis

4) Next, they test whether the hypothesis is right or not.
5) They do this by making a prediction — a statement based on the hypothesis that can be tested.
6) They then test this prediction by carrying out experiments.
7) If their prediction is right, this is evidence that their hypothesis might be right too.

Other scientists test the hypothesis too

8) Other scientists check the evidence — for example, they check that the experiment was carried out in a sensible way. This is called peer-review.
9) Scientists then share their results, e.g. in scientific papers.
10) Other scientists carry out more experiments to test the hypothesis.
11) Sometimes these scientists will find more evidence that the hypothesis is right.
12) Sometimes they'll find evidence that shows the hypothesis is wrong.

After more evidence was gathered, they changed their hypothesis to this.

The hypothesis is accepted or rejected

13) If all the evidence that's been found supports the hypothesis, it becomes an accepted theory and goes into textbooks for people to learn.
14) If the evidence shows that the hypothesis is wrong, scientists must:
   • Change the hypothesis, OR
   • Come up with a new hypothesis.

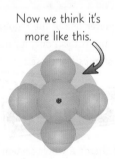

Now we think it's more like this.

Scientific models are constantly being improved...

The scientific method has been developed over time. Greek philosophers were the first people to realise that theories need to be based on observations. Muslim scholars then came up with the ideas of creating a hypothesis, testing it, and repeating work to check their results.

Models and Communication

Once scientists have made a <u>new discovery</u>, they <u>don't</u> just keep it to themselves. Oh no. Time to learn about how scientific discoveries are <u>communicated</u>, and the <u>models</u> that are used to represent theories.

Theories Can Involve **Different Types** of **Models**

1) A <u>model</u> is a <u>simple way</u> of <u>describing</u> or <u>showing</u> what's going on in <u>real life</u>.
2) Models can be used to <u>explain ideas</u> and <u>make predictions</u>. For example:

> • The <u>Bohr model</u> of an <u>atom</u> is a simple <u>picture</u> of what an atom looks like (see p.33).
> • It can be used to explain <u>trends</u> in the <u>periodic table</u> (see p.36 for more).

3) All models have <u>limits</u> — a single model <u>can't explain</u> everything about an idea.

It's Important to **Tell People** About Scientific Discoveries

1) Scientific discoveries can make a big difference to <u>people's lives</u>.
2) So scientists need to <u>tell the world</u> about their discoveries.
3) They might need to tell people to <u>change their habits</u>, e.g. stop smoking to protect against lung cancer.
4) They might also need to tell people about new <u>technologies</u>. For example:

> The discovery of molecules called <u>fullerenes</u> has led to a new technology that delivers medicine to <u>body cells</u>. <u>Doctors</u> and <u>patients</u> might need to be given <u>information</u> about this technology.

Scientific **Evidence** can be **Presented** in a **Biased Way**

1) <u>Reports</u> about scientific discoveries in the <u>media</u> (e.g. newspapers or television) can be <u>misleading</u>.
2) The data might be <u>presented</u> in a way that's <u>not quite right</u> — or it might be <u>oversimplified</u>.
3) This means that people may not <u>properly understand</u> what the scientists found out.
4) People who want to make a point can also sometimes <u>present data</u> in a <u>biased way</u> (in a way that's <u>unfair</u> or <u>ignores</u> one side of the argument). For example:

> • A <u>scientist</u> may talk a lot about <u>one particular relationship</u> in the data (and not mention others).
> • A <u>newspaper article</u> might describe data <u>supporting</u> an idea without giving any evidence <u>against</u> it.

Companies can present biased data to help sell products...

Sometimes a company may only want you to see half of the story so they present the data in a <u>biased way</u>. For example, a cleaning company may try and persuade you to buy their washing powder by telling you all the <u>positives</u>, but not telling you the results of any <u>unfavourable studies</u>.

Issues Created by Science

Science has helped us <u>make progress</u> in loads of areas, from medicine to space travel. But science still has its <u>issues</u>. And it <u>can't answer everything</u>, as you're about to find out.

Scientific Developments are Great, but they can Raise Issues

1) Scientific developments include <u>new technologies</u> and <u>new advice</u>.

2) These developments can create <u>issues</u>. For example:

> <u>Economic (money) issues:</u> Society <u>can't</u> always <u>afford</u> to do things scientists recommend, like spend money on green energy sources.

> <u>Social (people) issues:</u> Decisions based on scientific evidence affect <u>people</u> — e.g. should fossil fuels be taxed more (to help reduce climate change)?

> <u>Personal issues:</u> Some decisions will affect <u>individuals</u> — e.g. people may be upset if a <u>wind farm</u> is built next to their house.

> <u>Environmental issues:</u> <u>Human activity</u> often affects the <u>environment</u> — e.g. building a dam to produce electricity might cause <u>environmental problems</u> in the local area.

Science Can't Answer Every Question — Especially Ethical Ones

1) At the moment scientists <u>don't agree</u> on some things — like what the universe is made of.

2) This is because there <u>isn't</u> enough <u>data</u> to <u>support</u> the scientists' hypotheses.

3) But <u>eventually</u>, we probably <u>will</u> be able to answer these questions once and for all.

4) Experiments <u>can't tell us</u> whether something is <u>ethically right or wrong</u>. For example, whether it's right for people to use new drugs to help them do better in exams.

5) The best we can do is make a decision that <u>most people</u> are more or less happy to live by.

There are often issues with new scientific developments...

The trouble is, there's often <u>no clear right answer</u> where these issues are concerned. Different people have <u>different views</u>, depending on their priorities. These issues are full of <u>grey areas</u>.

Risk

Scientific discoveries are often great, but they can be risky. With dangers all around, you've got to look for hazards — this includes how likely they are to cause harm and how serious the effects may be.

Nothing is Completely Risk-Free

1) A hazard is something that could cause harm.

2) All hazards have a risk attached to them — this is the chance that the hazard will cause harm.

3) New technology can bring new risks. E.g. scientists are creating technology to capture and store carbon dioxide. But if the carbon dioxide leaked out it could damage soil or water supplies. These risks need to be considered alongside the benefits of the technology, e.g. lower greenhouse gas emissions.

4) To make a decision about activities that involve hazards, we need to think about:
   - the chance of the hazard causing harm,
   - how bad the outcome (consequences) would be if it did.

People Make Their Own Decisions About Risk

1) Not all risks have the same consequences. For example, if you chop veg with a sharp knife you risk cutting your finger, but if you go scuba-diving you risk death.
2) Most people are happier to accept a risk if the consequences don't last long and aren't serious.
3) People tend to think familiar activities are low-risk. They tend to think unfamiliar activities are high-risk. But this isn't always true. For example:

   - Cycling on roads is often high-risk. But it's a familiar activity, so many people are happy to do it.
   - Air travel is actually pretty safe, but a lot of people think it is high-risk.

4) The best way to estimate the size of a risk is to look at data. E.g. you could estimate the risk of a driver crashing by recording how many people in a group of 100 000 drivers crashed their cars over a year.

The pros and cons of new technology must be weighed up...

The world's a dangerous place and it's impossible to rule out the chance of an accident completely. But if you can recognise hazards and take steps to reduce the risks, you're more likely to stay safe.

Designing Investigations

Dig out your lab coat and dust down your safety goggles... it's <u>investigation time</u>.
Investigations include <u>lab experiments</u> and <u>studies</u> done in the <u>real world</u>.

Evidence Can Support or Disprove a Hypothesis

1) Scientists <u>observe</u> things and come up with <u>hypotheses</u> to explain them (see p.2).
   You need to be able to do the same. For example:

   > Observation: People have big feet and spots. Hypothesis: Having big feet causes spots.

2) To <u>find out</u> if your hypothesis is <u>right</u>, you need to do an <u>investigation</u> to gather evidence.

3) To do this, you need to use your hypothesis to make a <u>prediction</u> — something you think <u>will happen</u>
   that you can <u>test</u>. E.g. people who have bigger feet will have more spots.

4) Investigations are used to see if there are <u>patterns</u> or <u>relationships</u> between <u>two variables</u> (see below).

Make an Investigation a Fair Test By Controlling the Variables

1) In a lab experiment you usually <u>change one thing</u> (a variable)
   and <u>measure</u> how it affects <u>another thing</u> (another variable).

   > <u>Example:</u> you might <u>change</u> the <u>concentration</u> of a reactant
   > and <u>measure</u> how it affects the <u>temperature change</u> of the reaction.

2) <u>Everything else</u> that could affect the results needs to <u>stay the same</u>.
   Then you know that the thing you're <u>changing</u> is the <u>only</u> thing that's affecting the results.

   > <u>Example continued:</u> you need to keep the volume of the reactants the same.
   > If you don't, you won't know if any change in the temperature is caused by
   > the change in concentration, or the change in volume.

3) The variable that you <u>change</u> is called the <u>independent</u> variable.

4) The variable you <u>measure</u> is called the <u>dependent</u> variable.

5) The variables that you <u>keep the same</u> are called <u>control</u> variables.

6) Because you can't always control all the variables,
   you often need to use a <u>control experiment</u>.

> Example continued:
> Independent = concentration
> Dependent = temperature
> Control = volume of reactants,
>   pH, etc.

7) This is an experiment that's kept under the <u>same conditions</u> as the rest of the investigation, but <u>doesn't</u>
   have anything <u>done</u> to it. This is so that you can see what happens when you don't change <u>anything</u>.

Evidence Needs to be Repeatable, Reproducible and Valid

1) <u>Repeatable</u> means that if the <u>same person</u> does the experiment again, they'll get <u>similar results</u>.
   To check your results are repeatable, <u>repeat</u> the readings <u>at least three times</u>.
   Then check the repeat results are all similar.

2) <u>Reproducible</u> means that if <u>someone else</u> does the experiment, the results will still be <u>similar</u>.
   To make sure your results are reproducible, get <u>another person</u> to do the experiment too.

3) <u>Valid results</u> come from experiments that were designed to be a <u>fair test</u>.   If data is repeatable and reproducible,
   They're also repeatable and reproducible.   scientists are more likely to trust it.

Designing Investigations

The **Bigger** the **Sample Size** the **Better**

1) Sample size is <u>how many things you test</u> in an investigation, e.g. 500 people or 20 types of metal.

2) The <u>bigger</u> the sample size the <u>better</u> — to <u>reduce</u> the chance of any <u>weird results</u>.

3) But scientists have to be <u>realistic</u> when choosing how big their sample should be.
E.g. if you were studying the effects of a chemical used to sterilise water on the people drinking it, it'd be great to study everyone drinking the water (a huge sample), but it'd take ages and cost loads.

4) When you choose a sample, you need to make sure you've got a <u>range</u> of different people.

5) For example, both <u>men</u> and <u>women</u> with a range of <u>different ages</u>.

Your Data Should be **Accurate** and **Precise**

1) <u>Accurate results</u> are results that are <u>really close</u> to the <u>true answer</u>.

2) The accuracy of your results usually depends on your <u>method</u>. You need to make sure you're measuring the <u>right thing</u>.

3) You also need to make sure you <u>don't miss anything</u> that should be included in the measurements. For example:

> If you're measuring the <u>volume of gas</u> released by a reaction, make sure you <u>collect all the gas</u>.

4) <u>Precise results</u> are ones where the data is <u>all really close</u> to the <u>mean</u> (average) of your repeated results.

Repeat	Data set 1	Data set 2
1	12	11
2	14	17
3	13	14
Mean	<u>13</u>	<u>14</u>

Data set 1 is more precise than data set 2 — the results are all close to the mean (not spread out).

Your **Equipment** has to be **Right for the Job**

1) The <u>measuring equipment</u> you use has to be able to <u>accurately</u> measure the chemicals you're using. E.g. if you need to measure out 11 cm³ of a liquid, use a <u>measuring cylinder</u> that can measure to 1 cm³ — not 5 or 10 cm³.

2) You also need to <u>set up the equipment properly</u>. For example, make sure your <u>mass balance</u> is set to <u>zero</u> before you start weighing things.

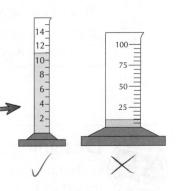

Designing Investigations

You Need to Look out for **Errors** and **Anomalous Results**

1) The results of your experiment will always <u>vary a bit</u> because of <u>random errors</u> — for example, mistakes you might make while <u>measuring</u>.

2) You can <u>reduce</u> the effect of random errors by taking <u>repeat readings</u> and finding the <u>mean</u>. This will make your results <u>more precise</u>.

3) If a measurement is wrong by the <u>same amount every time</u>, it's called a <u>systematic error</u>. For example:

> If you measure from the <u>very end</u> of your <u>ruler</u> instead of from the <u>0 cm mark</u> every time, <u>all</u> your measurements would be a bit <u>small</u>.

Always measure from here...
...not here.

4) If you know you've made a systematic error, you might be able to <u>correct it</u>. For example, by adding a bit on to all your measurements.

5) Sometimes you get a result that <u>doesn't fit in</u> with the rest. This is called an <u>anomalous result</u>.

6) You should try to <u>work out what happened</u>. If you do (e.g. you find out you measured something wrong) you can <u>ignore</u> it when processing your results (see next page).

Investigations Can Have **Hazards**

1) Hazards from science experiments include things like:

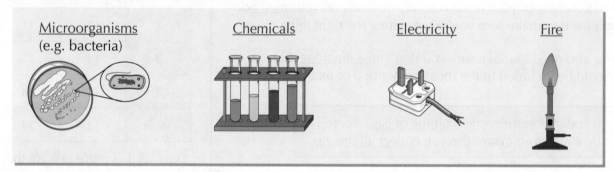

Microorganisms (e.g. bacteria) Chemicals Electricity Fire

2) When you <u>plan</u> an investigation you need to make sure that it's <u>safe</u>.

3) You should <u>identify</u> all the hazards that you might come across.

4) Then you should think of ways of <u>reducing the risks</u>. For example:

There's more on safety in experiments on page 149.

> • If you're working with <u>sulfuric acid</u>, always wear gloves and safety goggles. This will reduce the risk of the acid <u>burning</u> your skin and eyes.
>
> • If you're using a <u>Bunsen burner</u>, stand it on a heat proof mat. This will reduce the risk of starting a fire.

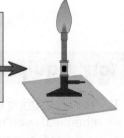

WORKING SCIENTIFICALLY

Designing an investigation is a long process...

Collecting <u>data</u> is what investigations are all about. Designing a good investigation is really important to make sure that any data collected is <u>accurate</u>, <u>precise</u>, <u>repeatable</u> and <u>reproducible</u>.

Processing Data

Processing your data means doing <u>calculations</u> with it so it's <u>more useful</u>.

Data Needs to be Organised

1) <u>Tables</u> are useful for <u>organising data</u>.

2) When you draw a table <u>use a ruler</u>.

3) Make sure <u>each column</u> has a <u>heading</u> (including the <u>units</u>).

Test tube	Repeat 1 (cm³)	Repeat 2 (cm³)
A	28	37
B	47	51

You Can Find the Mean, the Range, the Median or the Mode

1) When you've done repeats of an experiment you should always calculate the <u>mean</u> (a type of average).

2) You might also need to calculate the <u>range</u> (how spread out the data is).

EXAMPLE: **The results of an experiment to find the volume of gas produced in a reaction are shown in the table below. Calculate the mean volume and the range.**

Volume of gas produced (cm³)		
Repeat 1	Repeat 2	Repeat 3
28	37	31

1) To calculate the <u>mean</u>, <u>add together</u> all the data values. Then <u>divide</u> by the <u>total number</u> of values in the sample.

$(28 + 37 + 31) \div 3 = 32$ cm³

2) To calculate the <u>range</u>, <u>subtract</u> the <u>smallest</u> number from the <u>largest</u> number.

$37 - 28 = 9$ cm³

3) To find the <u>median</u>, put all your data in <u>order</u> from smallest to largest. The median is the <u>middle value</u>.

4) The number that appears <u>most often</u> is the <u>mode</u>.

E.g. if you have the data set: 1 2 1 1 3 4 2
The <u>median</u> is: 1 1 1 <u>2</u> 2 3 4.
The <u>mode</u> is <u>1</u> because 1 appears most often.

If you have an even number of values, the median is halfway between the middle two values.

5) When calculating any of these values, always <u>ignore</u> any <u>anomalous results</u>.

Round to the Lowest Number of Significant Figures

1) The <u>first significant figure</u> of a number is the first digit that's <u>not zero</u>.

2) The second and third significant figures come <u>straight after</u> (even if they're zeros).

3) In <u>any</u> calculation, you should round the answer to the <u>lowest number of significant figures</u> (s.f.) given.

4) If your calculation has more than one step, <u>only</u> round the <u>final</u> answer.

1st significant figure

0.0307

2nd   3rd

EXAMPLE: **The mass of a solid is 0.24 g and its volume is 0.715 cm³. Calculate the density of the solid.**

Density = 0.24 g ÷ 0.715 cm³ = 0.33566... = 0.34 g/cm³ (2 s.f.)

2 s.f.   3 s.f.

Final answer should be rounded to 2 s.f.

Presenting Data

Once you've processed your data, e.g. by calculating the mean, you can present your results in a nice <u>chart</u> or <u>graph</u>. This will help you to <u>spot any patterns</u> in your data.

If Your Data Comes in **Categories**, Present It in a **Bar Chart**

If the independent variable comes in <u>clear categories</u> (e.g. fractions of crude oil, types of metal) or can be <u>counted exactly</u> (e.g. number of protons) you should use a <u>bar chart</u> to display the data. Here's what to do:

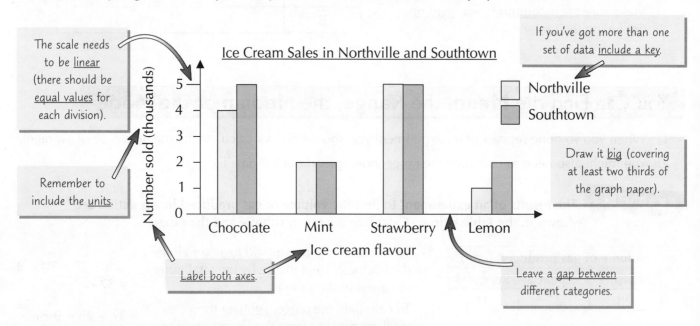

The scale needs to be <u>linear</u> (there should be <u>equal values</u> for each division).

If you've got more than one set of data <u>include a key</u>.

Remember to include the <u>units</u>.

Draw it <u>big</u> (covering at least two thirds of the graph paper).

Label both axes.

Leave a <u>gap between</u> different categories.

If Your Data is **Continuous**, Plot a **Graph**

1) If both variables can have any value <u>within a range</u> (e.g. length, volume) use a <u>graph</u> to display the data.

2) Here are the rules for plotting points on a graph:

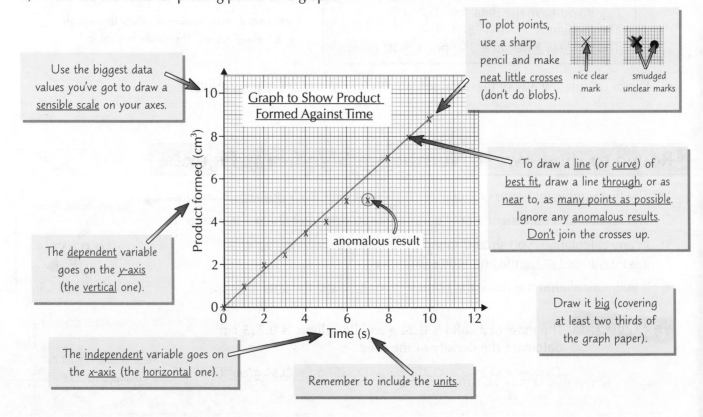

Use the biggest data values you've got to draw a <u>sensible scale</u> on your axes.

To plot points, use a sharp pencil and make <u>neat little crosses</u> (don't do blobs).

nice clear mark — smudged unclear marks

To draw a <u>line</u> (or <u>curve</u>) of <u>best fit</u>, draw a line <u>through</u>, or as <u>near</u> to, as <u>many points as possible</u>. Ignore any <u>anomalous results</u>. <u>Don't</u> join the crosses up.

The <u>dependent</u> variable goes on the <u>y-axis</u> (the <u>vertical</u> one).

Draw it <u>big</u> (covering at least two thirds of the graph paper).

The <u>independent</u> variable goes on the <u>x-axis</u> (the <u>horizontal</u> one).

Remember to include the <u>units</u>.

More on Graphs

Graph's aren't just fun to plot, they're also really useful for showing <u>trends</u> in your data.

You Can Calculate the **Rate** of Reaction from the **Gradient** of a Graph

1) This is the <u>formula</u> you need to calculate the <u>gradient</u> (slope) of a graph:

$$\text{gradient} = \frac{\text{change in } y}{\text{change in } x}$$

 To calculate a rate, the graph must have time on the *x*-axis.

2) You can use it to work out the <u>rate of a reaction</u> (how <u>quickly</u> the reaction happens).

EXAMPLE:

The graph shows the volume of gas produced in a reaction against time. Calculate the rate of reaction.

1) To calculate the <u>gradient</u>, pick <u>two points</u> on the line that are easy to read. They should also be a <u>good distance</u> apart.

2) Draw a line <u>down</u> from the higher point. Then draw a line <u>across</u> from the other, to make a <u>triangle</u>.

3) The line drawn <u>down the side</u> of the triangle is the <u>change in y</u>. The line <u>across the bottom</u> is the <u>change in x</u>.

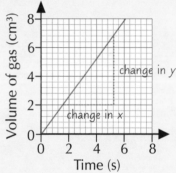

4) Read the *x* and *y* values of the points <u>off the graph</u> and work out the change in *y* and the change in *x*:

Change in $y = 6.8 - 2.0 = 4.8 \text{ cm}^3$ Change in $x = 5.2 - 1.6 = 3.6$ s

5) Then put these numbers in the formula above to find the rate of the reaction:

$$\text{Rate} = \text{gradient} = \frac{\text{change in } y}{\text{change in } x} = \frac{4.8 \text{ cm}^3}{3.6 \text{ s}} = 1.33... = 1.3 \text{ cm}^3/\text{s (2 s.f.)}$$

The units are (units of *y*)/(units of *x*). cm^3/s can also be written as $\text{cm}^3 \text{ s}^{-1}$.

Graphs Show the **Relationship** Between Two Variables

1) You can get <u>three</u> types of <u>correlation</u> (relationship) between variables:

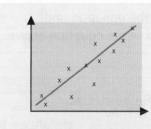

<u>POSITIVE correlation:</u> as one variable <u>increases</u> the other <u>increases</u>.

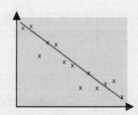

<u>INVERSE (negative) correlation:</u> as one variable <u>increases</u> the other <u>decreases</u>.

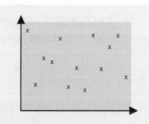

<u>NO correlation:</u> <u>no relationship</u> between the two variables.

2) A correlation <u>doesn't mean</u> the change in one variable is <u>causing</u> the change in the other (see page 14).

MATHS TIP

You need to learn the formula for calculating a gradient

Remember — the *x*-axis is the one that goes across the bottom, because x is a cross...

Units and Equations

Graphs and maths skills are all very well, but the numbers don't mean much if you don't get the <u>units</u> right. It's also really useful to know how to <u>rearrange</u> an <u>equation</u> — this page will show you how.

S.I. Units Are Used All Round the World

1) All scientists use the same <u>units</u> to measure their data.

2) These are <u>standard units</u>, called S.I. units.

3) Here are some S.I. units you might see:

Quantity	S.I. Base Unit
mass	kilogram, kg
length	metre, m
time	second, s
temperature	kelvin, K

You Can **Rearrange** Equations

1) Equations show <u>relationships</u> between <u>variables</u>. For example, $\text{speed} = \dfrac{\text{distance}}{\text{time}}$.

2) The <u>subject</u> of an equation is the variable <u>by itself</u> on one side of the equals sign. So <u>speed</u> is the <u>subject</u> in the equation above.

3) To <u>change</u> the <u>subject</u> of an equation do the same thing to <u>both sides</u> of the equation until you've got the subject you <u>want</u>. E.g. you can make <u>distance</u> the subject of the equation above:

<u>Multiply</u> both sides by <u>time</u>: $\quad \text{speed} = \dfrac{\text{distance}}{\text{time}} \quad \Longrightarrow \quad \text{speed} \times \text{time} = \dfrac{\text{distance} \times \text{time}}{\text{time}}$

Time is now on the top <u>and</u> the bottom of the fraction, so it cancels out: $\quad \text{speed} \times \text{time} = \dfrac{\text{distance} \times \cancel{\text{time}}}{\cancel{\text{time}}}$

This leaves <u>distance</u> by itself. So it's the <u>subject</u>: $\quad \text{speed} \times \text{time} = \text{distance}$

S.I. units help scientists to compare data...

You can only really <u>compare</u> things if they're in the <u>same units</u>. E.g. if the concentration of an acid was measured in g/dm^3 and another acid in g/cm^3, it'd be hard to compare them.

Converting Units

You can convert units using scaling prefixes. I know that sounds a bit maths-y, but don't worry — things will all become clear as you work through this next page.

Different Units Help you to Write Large and Small Quantities

1) Quantities come in a huge range of sizes.
2) To make the size of numbers easier to handle, larger or smaller units are used.
3) Larger and smaller units are written as the S.I. base unit with a little word in front (a prefix). Here are some examples of prefixes and what they mean:

Kilogram is an exception. It's an S.I. unit with the prefix already on it.

Prefix	mega (M)	kilo (k)	deci (d)	centi (c)	milli (m)	micro (μ)
How it compares to the base unit	1 000 000 times bigger	1000 times bigger	10 times smaller	100 times smaller	1000 times smaller	1 000 000 times smaller

E.g. 1 kilometre is 1000 metres.　　　E.g. there are 1000 millimetres in 1 metre.

You Need to be Able to Convert Between Units

You need to know how to convert (change) one unit into another. Here are some useful conversions:

Multiply to go from a bigger unit to a smaller unit.

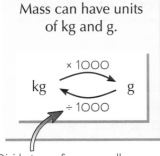

Mass can have units of kg and g.

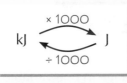

Energy can have units of J and kJ.

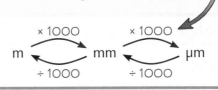

Length can have lots of units, including m, mm and μm.

Divide to go from a smaller unit to a bigger unit.

Always make sure the values you put into an equation or formula have the right units.

EXAMPLE: **A scientist has a sample of a compound with a mass of 0.015 kilograms. What is the mass of the sample in grams?**

1 kg = 1000 g. So to convert from kg (a bigger unit) to g (a smaller unit) you need to multiply by 1000.

0.015 kg × 1000 = 15 g

 MATHS TIP

Make sure you learn all of the prefixes that can go before a unit

If you're moving from a smaller unit to a larger unit (e.g. g to kg) the number should get smaller, and vice versa. You can use this to check to see if you've done the calculation correctly. E.g. if you tried to convert from J to kJ and the number got bigger, something's gone a bit wrong.

Drawing Conclusions

Once you've carried out an experiment and processed your data, it's time to work out what your data shows.

You Can **Only Conclude** What the Data Shows and **No More**

1) To come to a conclusion, look at your data and say what pattern you see.

	Catalyst	Rate of Reaction / cm³/s	

Example: The table on the right shows the rate of a reaction in the presence of two different catalysts:

Catalyst	Rate of Reaction / cm³/s
A	13.5
B	19.5
No catalyst	5.5

CONCLUSION: Catalyst B makes this reaction go faster than catalyst A.

2) It's important that the conclusion matches the data it's based on — it shouldn't go any further.

Example continued: You can't conclude that catalyst B increases the rate of any other reaction more than catalyst A — the results might be completely different.

3) You also need to be able to use your results to justify your conclusion (i.e. back it up).

Example continued: The rate of this reaction was 6 cm³/s faster using catalyst B compared with catalyst A.

4) When writing a conclusion you need to say whether or not the data supports the original hypothesis:

Example continued: The hypothesis for this experiment might have been that catalyst B would make the reaction go quicker than catalyst A. If so, the data supports the hypothesis.

Correlation **DOES NOT** Mean **Cause**

1) If two things are correlated, there's a relationship between them — see page 11.
2) But a correlation doesn't always mean that a change in one variable is causing the change in the other.
3) There are three possible reasons for a correlation:

Chance
The results happened by chance. Other scientists wouldn't get a correlation if they carried out the same investigation.

Linked by a 3rd variable
There's another factor involved.

E.g. there's a correlation between water temperature and shark attacks. They're linked by a third variable — the number of people swimming (more people swim when the water's hotter, which means you get more shark attacks).

Cause
Sometimes a change in one variable does cause a change in the other. You can only conclude this when you've controlled all the variables that could be affecting the result.

Uncertainty

Uncertainty is how sure you can really be about your data. There's a little bit of maths to do, and also a formula to learn. But don't worry too much — it's no more than a simple bit of subtraction and division.

Uncertainty is the Amount of Error Your Measurements Might Have

1) Measurements you make will have some uncertainty in them (i.e. they won't be completely perfect).

2) This can be due to random errors (see page 8).
It can also be due to limits in what your measuring equipment can measure.

3) This means that the mean of your results will have some uncertainty to it.

4) You can calculate the uncertainty of a mean result using this equation:

$$\text{uncertainty} = \frac{\text{range}}{2}$$

The range is the largest value minus the smallest value (p.9).

5) The less precise your results are, the higher the uncertainty will be.

6) Uncertainties are shown using the '±' symbol — this symbol stands for 'plus or minus'.
It shows the maximum possible difference between your mean value and the true value.

> For example, a mean of 1.5 cm³ with an uncertainty of ± 0.1 cm³ means that the true value for the mean could be anywhere between 1.5 − 0.1 = 1.4 cm³ to 1.5 + 0.1 = 1.6 cm³.

EXAMPLE:

The table below shows the results of an experiment to find the boiling point of ethanol.

Calculate the uncertainty of the mean.

1) First work out the range:

Range = 80 − 76 = 4 °C

Repeat	1	2	3	mean
Boiling point of ethanol (°C)	76	78	80	78

2) Use the range to find the uncertainty:

Uncertainty = range ÷ 2 = 4 ÷ 2 = 2 °C

So the uncertainty of the mean = 78 ± 2 °C

The smaller the uncertainty, the more precise your results...

Remember that equation for uncertainty. You never know when you might need it — you could be expected to use it in the exams. You need to make sure all the data is in the same units though. For example, if you had some measurements in metres, and some in centimetres, you'd need to convert them all into either metres or centimetres before you set about calculating uncertainty.

Evaluations

Hurrah! The end of another investigation. Well, now you have to work out all the things you did <u>wrong</u>. That's what <u>evaluations</u> are all about I'm afraid. Best get cracking with this page...

Evaluations — Describe **How** it Could be **Improved**

In an evaluation you look back over the whole investigation.

1) You should comment on the <u>method</u> — was it <u>valid</u>?
   Did you control all the other variables to make it a <u>fair test</u>?

2) Comment on the <u>quality</u> of the <u>results</u> — was there <u>enough evidence</u> to reach a valid <u>conclusion</u>?
   Were the results <u>repeatable</u>, <u>reproducible</u>, <u>accurate</u> and <u>precise</u>?

3) Were there any <u>anomalous</u> results? If there were <u>none</u> then <u>say so</u>.
   If there were any, try to <u>explain</u> them — were they caused by <u>errors</u> in measurement?

4) You should comment on the level of <u>uncertainty</u> in your results too.

5) Thinking about these things lets you say how <u>confident</u> you are that your conclusion is <u>right</u>.

6) Then you can suggest any <u>changes</u> to the <u>method</u> that would <u>improve</u> the
   quality of the results, so you could have <u>more confidence</u> in your conclusion.

7) For example, taking measurements at <u>narrower intervals</u> could give you a <u>more accurate result</u>.

- Say you do an experiment to find the <u>temperature</u> at which an enzyme <u>works best</u>.
- You take measurements at <u>30 °C</u>, <u>40 °C</u> and <u>50 °C</u>.
  The results show that the enzyme works best at <u>40 °C</u>.
- To get a more accurate result, you could <u>repeat</u> the experiment and take <u>more measurements</u>
  <u>around 40 °C</u>. You might then find that the enzyme actually works best at <u>42 °C</u>.

8) You could also make more <u>predictions</u> based on your conclusion.
   You could then carry out <u>further experiments</u> to test the new predictions.

Always look for ways to improve your investigations

So there you have it — <u>Working Scientifically</u>. Make sure you know this stuff like the back of your hand. It's not just in the lab or the field, when you're carrying out your <u>investigations</u>, that you'll need to know how to work scientifically. You can be asked about it in the <u>exams</u> as well. So get revising...

Atoms

All substances are made of <u>atoms</u>. They're really <u>tiny</u> — too small to see, even with your microscope. Atoms are so tiny that a <u>50p piece</u> contains about 77 400 000 000 000 000 000 000 of them.

Atoms Contain **Protons, Neutrons** and **Electrons**

Atoms have a radius of about <u>0.1 nanometers</u> (that's 1×10^{-10} m). There are a few different modern models of the atom — but chemists tend to like the model on the right best.

A nanometer (nm) is 0.000000001 m. Shown in standard form, that's 1×10^{-9} m. Standard form is used for showing really large or really small numbers.

atomic radius

The **Nucleus**

1) It's in the <u>middle</u> of the atom.

2) It contains <u>protons</u> and <u>neutrons</u>.

3) The nucleus has a <u>radius</u> of around 1×10^{-14} m (that's around 1/10 000 of the atomic radius).

4) It has a <u>positive charge</u> because of the protons.

5) Almost the <u>whole</u> mass of the atom is in the nucleus.

The **Electrons**

1) Move <u>around</u> the nucleus in electron <u>shells</u> (levels).

2) They're <u>negatively charged</u>.

3) Electrons have almost <u>no</u> mass.

Particle	Relative Mass	Relative Charge
Proton	1	+1
Neutron	1	0
Electron	Very small	−1

You need to know the <u>charges</u> of protons, neutrons and electrons.
You also need to know how <u>heavy</u> they are compared to each other (their <u>relative masses</u>).

- <u>Protons</u> are <u>heavy</u> (compared to electrons) and <u>positively</u> charged.
- <u>Neutrons</u> are <u>heavy</u> (compared to electrons) and <u>neutral</u>.
- <u>Electrons</u> are <u>tiny</u> and <u>negatively</u> charged.

Atomic Number and **Mass Number** Describe an Atom

1) The <u>nuclear symbol</u> of an atom tells you its <u>atomic (proton) number</u> and <u>mass number</u>.

> <u>atomic number</u> = number of protons
> <u>mass number</u> = number of protons + number of neutrons
> <u>number of neutrons</u> = mass number − atomic number

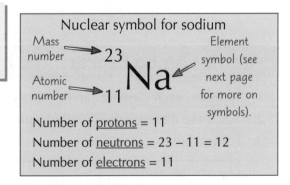

Nuclear symbol for sodium

Mass number → 23
Atomic number → 11 **Na** ← Element symbol (see next page for more on symbols).

Number of <u>protons</u> = 11
Number of <u>neutrons</u> = 23 − 11 = 12
Number of <u>electrons</u> = 11

2) Atoms have <u>no charge</u> overall. They're neutral.

3) This is because they have the <u>same number</u> of <u>protons</u> as <u>electrons</u>. So, in an atom...

> <u>number of electrons</u> = atomic number

4) The <u>charge</u> on the electrons is the <u>same size</u> as the charge on the <u>protons</u>, but <u>opposite</u>. So they <u>cancel out</u>.

5) In an <u>ion</u>, the number of protons <u>doesn't equal</u> the number of <u>electrons</u>. This means it has an <u>overall charge</u>. For example, an ion with a <u>2− charge</u>, has <u>two more</u> electrons than protons.

> In a <u>positive</u> ion: <u>number of electrons</u> = atomic number − charge
> In a <u>negative</u> ion: <u>number of electrons</u> = atomic number + charge

An ion is an atom or group of atoms that has lost or gained electrons.

Elements

An <u>element</u> is a substance made up of atoms that all have the <u>same</u> number of <u>protons</u> in their nucleus.

Elements are Made Up of **Atoms** With the **Same Atomic Number**

1) The <u>smallest part</u> of an element that you can have is a <u>single atom</u> of that element.

2) The number of <u>protons</u> in the nucleus decides what <u>type</u> of atom it is.

> For example, an atom with <u>one proton</u> in its nucleus is <u>hydrogen</u>. An atom with <u>two protons</u> is <u>helium</u>.

3) If a substance only contains atoms with the <u>same number</u> of <u>protons</u> it's called an <u>element</u>.

4) So <u>all the atoms</u> of a particular <u>element</u> have the <u>same number</u> of protons. And <u>different elements</u> have atoms with <u>different numbers</u> of protons.

5) There are about <u>100 different elements</u>. Each element is made up of only one type of atom — some examples are shown in the diagram below.

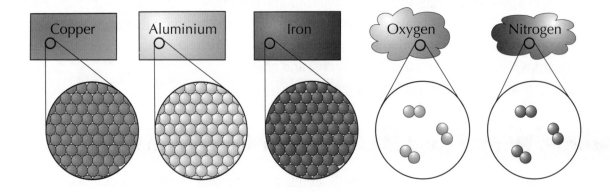

Atoms Can be Represented by **Symbols**

1) Atoms of each element can be represented by a <u>one or two letter symbol</u>.
2) You'll see these symbols on the periodic table (see page 36).
3) For example:

| C = carbon | O = oxygen | Na = sodium | Mg = magnesium | Fe = iron |

All atoms in an element have the same number of protons

<u>Atoms</u> and <u>elements</u> — make sure you know what they are and the <u>differences</u> between them. You don't need to learn all the symbols as you can use a <u>periodic table</u>, but it's handy to know the common ones.

Isotopes

What's inside different atoms of the <u>same element</u> can vary. Read on to find out how...

Isotopes are the Same Except for Extra **Neutrons**

1) <u>Isotopes</u> are:

> Atoms with the <u>same</u> number of <u>protons</u> but a <u>different</u> number of <u>neutrons</u>

2) So they have the <u>same atomic number</u> but <u>different mass numbers</u>.

3) Carbon-12 and carbon-13 are isotopes of <u>carbon</u>.

Carbon-12

6 PROTONS
6 ELECTRONS
6 NEUTRONS

$^{12}_{6}\text{C}$

The number of neutrons is the mass number minus the atomic number.

Carbon-13

6 PROTONS
6 ELECTRONS
7 NEUTRONS

$^{13}_{6}\text{C}$

4) If an element has a number of isotopes, you can describe it using <u>relative atomic mass</u> (A_r) instead of mass number. This is an <u>average</u> mass.

You can work out the 'sum of' two or more amounts by adding them together.

5) A_r is worked out from the <u>different masses</u> and <u>abundances</u> (amounts) of each isotope.

6) You can use this <u>formula</u> to work out the <u>relative atomic mass</u> of an element:

$$\text{relative atomic mass } (A_r) = \frac{\text{sum of (isotope abundance} \times \text{isotope mass number)}}{\text{sum of abundances of all the isotopes}}$$

EXAMPLE: **Copper has two stable isotopes. Cu-63 has an abundance of 69.2% and Cu-65 has an abundance of 30.8%. Calculate the relative atomic mass of copper to 1 decimal place.**

abundance × mass number of Cu-63   abundance × mass number of Cu-65

$$\text{Relative atomic mass} = \frac{(69.2 \times 63) + (30.8 \times 65)}{69.2 + 30.8} = \frac{4359.6 + 2002}{100} = \frac{6361.6}{100} = 63.616 = 63.6$$

abundance of Cu-63 + abundance of Cu-65

Relative atomic mass is the average atomic mass of an element

Relative atomic mass takes into account <u>all</u> isotopes of an element — this is <u>different</u> to the <u>mass number</u>, which is the <u>mass</u> of a <u>just one isotope</u> of an element. Make sure you remember the difference.

Compounds

It would be great if we only had to deal with elements. But unluckily for you, elements can mix and match to make lots of new substances called <u>compounds</u>. And this makes things a little bit more complicated...

Atoms **Join Together** to Make **Compounds**

1) During a chemical reaction, at least one <u>new</u> substance is made.
   You can usually measure a <u>change in energy</u> such as a temperature change, as well.

2) When <u>two or more elements react</u>, they form <u>compounds</u>.
   <u>Compounds</u> are substances that contain atoms of different elements.

3) The atoms of each element are in <u>fixed proportions</u> (amounts) in the compound.

4) The atoms are held together by <u>chemical bonds</u>.

5) The only way to <u>separate</u> a compound into its elements is by using a <u>chemical reaction</u>.

There are different types of compound. For example, ionic compounds (see p.49-51) and covalent compounds (see p.53-55).

A **Formula** Shows What **Atoms** are in a **Compound**

1) Compounds can be represented by <u>formulas</u>.

2) The formulas are made up of element symbols in the <u>same proportions</u> as the elements in the compound.

3) The <u>number</u> of different element symbols tells you <u>how many</u> elements are in the compound.

- For example, carbon dioxide, CO_2, is a <u>compound</u> made from a <u>reaction</u> between carbon and oxygen.
- It contains <u>1 carbon atom</u> and <u>2 oxygen atoms</u>.

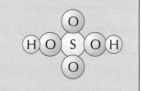

carbon + oxygen → carbon dioxide

As an element, oxygen goes around in pairs of atoms (so it's O_2).

- Here's another example: the formula of <u>sulfuric acid</u> is H_2SO_4.
- So, each molecule contains <u>2 hydrogen atoms</u>, <u>1 sulfur atom</u> and <u>4 oxygen atoms</u>.

- There might be <u>brackets</u> in a formula, e.g. calcium hydroxide is $Ca(OH)_2$.
- The little number <u>2</u> outside the bracket means there's <u>two of everything</u> inside the brackets.
- So in $Ca(OH)_2$ there's <u>1 calcium atom</u>, <u>2 oxygen atoms</u> and <u>2 hydrogen atoms</u>.

4) Here are some examples of formulas which might come in handy:

Carbon dioxide — CO_2	Sodium chloride — $NaCl$	Calcium chloride — $CaCl_2$
Ammonia — NH_3	Carbon monoxide — CO	Sodium carbonate — Na_2CO_3
Water — H_2O	Hydrochloric acid — HCl	Sulfuric acid — H_2SO_4

EXAM TIP

The atoms in compounds are chemically joined

In your exams, you could be asked to give the name of a compound from its formula. Make sure you get lots of <u>practice</u> using the <u>periodic table</u> to find which elements the different <u>symbols</u> stand for — you'll save a lot of time if you <u>already know</u> where to look.

Chemical Equations

Chemical equations are used to show what is happening to substances involved in chemical reactions. They tell us what atoms are involved and how the substances change during a reaction.

Chemical Reactions are Shown Using Chemical Equations

1) One way to show a chemical reaction is to write a word equation.

2) Word equations show the names of the chemicals that are reacting and being produced.

Here's an example — methane reacts with oxygen to make carbon dioxide and water:

methane + oxygen → carbon dioxide + water

The chemicals on the left-hand side of the equation are called the reactants (because they react with each other).

The chemicals on the right-hand side are called the products (because they've been produced from the reactants).

Symbol Equations Show the Atoms on Both Sides

1) Chemical reactions can be shown using symbol equations.

2) Symbol equations just show the symbols or formulas of the reactants and products.

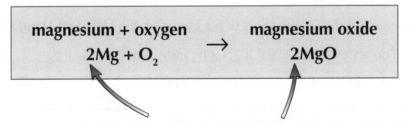

magnesium + oxygen → magnesium oxide
$$2Mg + O_2 \rightarrow 2MgO$$

You'll have spotted that there's a '2' in front of the Mg and the MgO. The reason for this is explained on the next page...

Symbol equations give you extra information

Writing symbol equations makes it easier to see how many atoms are involved in a reaction, and where they all end up. It also saves quite a lot of time, so it's no wonder scientists prefer them to word equations. You'll need to make sure you're comfortable using both for your exams though.

Chemical Equations

Symbol Equations Need to be Balanced

1) There must always be the <u>same</u> number of atoms on <u>both sides</u> — they can't just <u>disappear</u>.
2) You <u>balance</u> the equation by putting numbers <u>in front</u> of the formulas.
   Take this equation for reacting sulfuric acid with sodium hydroxide:

$$H_2SO_4 + NaOH \rightarrow Na_2SO_4 + H_2O$$

Left-hand side	Right-hand side
H = 3	H = 2
S = 1	S = 1
O = 5	O = 5
Na = 1	Na = 2

3) The <u>formulas</u> are all correct but the numbers of some atoms <u>don't match up</u> on both sides.
4) This equation needs <u>balancing</u> — see below for how to do this.

Here's How to Balance an Equation

The more you <u>practise</u>, the <u>quicker</u> you get, but all you do is this:

1) Find an element that <u>doesn't balance</u> and <u>pencil in a number</u> in front of one of the substances to try and sort it out.
2) <u>See where it gets you</u>. The equation may still <u>not</u> be balanced. Don't worry, just pencil in <u>another number</u> and see where that gets you.
3) Keep doing this until the equation is <u>completely balanced</u>.

You can't change formulas like H_2SO_4 to H_2SO_5. You can only put numbers in front of them.

EXAMPLE:

In the equation above you'll notice we're short of <u>Na atoms</u> on the LHS (Left-Hand Side).

1) The only thing you can do about that is make it <u>2NaOH</u> instead of just NaOH:

$$H_2SO_4 + 2NaOH \rightarrow Na_2SO_4 + H_2O$$

LHS	RHS
H = 4	H = 2
S = 1	S = 1
O = 6	O = 5
Na = 2	Na = 2

2) But that now gives <u>too many</u> H atoms and O atoms on the LHS. So to balance that up you could try putting <u>2H₂O</u> on the RHS (Right-Hand Side):

$$H_2SO_4 + 2NaOH \rightarrow Na_2SO_4 + 2H_2O$$

3) And suddenly there it is — <u>everything balances</u>.

Getting good at balancing equations takes patience and practice

Remember, a number <u>in front</u> of a formula applies to the <u>entire formula</u> — so, $3CH_4$ means three lots of CH_4. The little numbers <u>within or at the end</u> of a formula only apply to the <u>atom or brackets</u> immediately before. So the 4 in CH_4 means there are 4 Hs, but there's just 1 C, not 4.

Warm-Up & Exam Questions

So, you reckon you know your elements from your compounds? Have a go at these questions and see how you do. If you get stuck on something, just flick back and give it another read through.

Warm-Up Questions

1) What does the mass number tell you about an atom?
2) What is the definition of an element?
3) True or false? A compound may contain atoms of only one element.
4) Name the compound that has the formula $CaCl_2$.
5) Balance this equation for the reaction of potassium (K) and water (H_2O):
   $K + H_2O \rightarrow KOH + H_2$

Exam Questions

1 This question is about atomic structure. Grade 1-3

1.1 Which row of **Table 1** correctly shows the relative charges of a proton and a neutron?
Tick **one** box.

Table 1

Relative charge of a proton	Relative charge of a neutron	
+1	−1	☐
+1	0	☐
0	+1	☐
−1	0	☐

[1 mark]

1.2 Where are protons and neutrons found in an atom?
Tick **one** box.

☐ spread around the atom   ☐ in shells around the nucleus   ☐ in the nucleus   ☐ in the electrons

[1 mark]

1.3 An atom has 8 electrons. How many protons does the atom have?

[1 mark]

1.4 What is the relative mass of a proton?

[1 mark]

2 **Table 2** gives some information about sodium. Grade 3-4

Table 2

Element	Number of protons	Mass number
sodium	11	23

2.1 How many neutrons does sodium have?

[1 mark]

2.2 Give the atomic number of sodium.

[1 mark]

2.3 What is the chemical symbol for sodium?

[1 mark]

Exam Questions

3   Methane (CH_4) reacts with oxygen (O_2) to make carbon dioxide (CO_2) and water (H_2O).   **Grade 3-4**

3.1 Give the names of the reactants in this reaction.

[1 mark]

3.2 Give the names of the products in this reaction.

[1 mark]

3.3 Which molecule involved in the reaction is composed of only one element?

[1 mark]

3.4 Balance the symbol equation for the reaction below.

$$CH_4 \ + \ ....O_2 \ \rightarrow \ CO_2 \ + \ ....H_2O$$

[1 mark]

4   Sulfuric acid (H_2SO_4) reacts with ammonia (NH_3) to form ammonium sulfate, $(NH_4)_2SO_4$.   **Grade 4-5**

4.1 Complete and balance the symbol equation below.

$$................. \ + \ .... \ \rightarrow \ (NH_4)_2SO_4$$

[2 marks]

4.2 How many different elements are there in this reaction?

[1 mark]

4.3 How many hydrogen atoms are there in the formula of ammonium sulfate?

[1 mark]

5   The element boron has two isotopes, boron-10 and boron-11.   **Grade 4-5**
      Details about the boron-11 isotope are shown below.

$$^{11}_{5}B$$

5.1 Complete the sentence below explaining what an isotope is. Use words from the box.

protons	shells	neutrons	nuclei	electrons

Isotopes are different forms of the same element, which have the

same number of .... but different numbers of ....

[2 marks]

5.2 How many protons are there in an atom of boron-11?

[1 mark]

5.3 Boron-10 has a mass number of 10 and a percentage abundance of 20%.
       Boron-11 has a mass number of 11 and a percentage abundance of 80%.
       Use the equation below to calculate the relative atomic mass of boron.

$$\text{relative atomic mass} = \frac{\text{sum of (isotope abundance} \times \text{isotope mass number)}}{\text{sum of abundances of all the isotopes}}$$

[3 marks]

Topic 1 — Atomic Structure and the Periodic Table

Mixtures

Mixtures in <u>chemistry</u> are just like mixtures in everyday life, lots of <u>separate</u> things all mixed together.

Mixtures are Easily Separated — Not Like Compounds

1) Mixtures contain <u>at least two</u> different <u>elements</u> or <u>compounds</u>.
2) There <u>aren't</u> any <u>chemical bonds</u> between the different parts of a mixture.

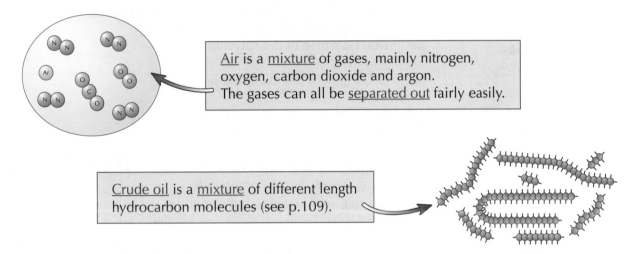

<u>Air</u> is a <u>mixture</u> of gases, mainly nitrogen, oxygen, carbon dioxide and argon.
The gases can all be <u>separated out</u> fairly easily.

<u>Crude oil</u> is a <u>mixture</u> of different length hydrocarbon molecules (see p.109).

3) The different parts of a mixture can be <u>separated</u> out by <u>methods</u> such as:

- filtration (p.27)
- crystallisation (p.27)
- simple distillation (p.29)
- fractional distillation (p.30)
- chromatography (p.26)

4) The methods are all <u>physical methods</u>.
This means they <u>don't</u> involve any chemical reactions, and don't form any new substances.

Each Part of a Mixture Keeps Its Own Properties

1) Properties describe what a substance is <u>like</u> and how it <u>behaves</u>, such as hardness or boiling point.
2) The <u>properties</u> of a mixture are just a <u>mixture</u> of the properties of the <u>separate parts</u>.
The chemical properties of a substance <u>aren't</u> changed by it being part of a mixture.

For example, a <u>mixture</u> of <u>iron powder</u> and <u>sulfur powder</u> will show the <u>properties</u> of <u>both</u> iron and sulfur. It will contain grey magnetic bits of iron and bright yellow bits of sulfur.

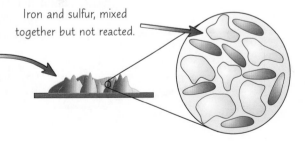

Iron and sulfur, mixed together but not reacted.

Mixtures can be separated without a chemical reaction

Remember that the different parts of mixtures <u>aren't joined together chemically</u>. This means their chemical properties are <u>not changed</u> and the compounds or elements can be separated by <u>physical methods</u>.

Chromatography

Paper chromatography is a really useful technique to separate the compounds in a mixture.

You Need to Know How to Do **Paper Chromatography**

One method of separating substances in a mixture is chromatography.
Chromatography can be used to separate different dyes in an ink. Here's how you can do it:

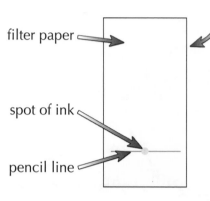

filter paper

spot of ink

pencil line

1) Draw a line near the bottom of a sheet of filter paper.
   (Use a pencil to do this — pencil marks won't dissolve in the solvent.)

2) Add a spot of the ink to the line.

3) Pour a small amount of solvent into a beaker so it forms a shallow layer.

4) The solvent used depends on what's being tested. Some compounds dissolve well in water, but sometimes other solvents, like ethanol, are needed.

A solvent is a liquid which dissolves another substance.

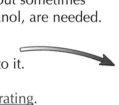

5) Place the sheet in the beaker of solvent. Make sure the ink isn't touching the solvent — you don't want it to dissolve into it.

6) Place a lid on top of the container to stop the solvent evaporating.

7) The solvent seeps up the paper, carrying the ink with it.

8) When the solvent has nearly reached the top of the paper, take the paper out of the beaker and leave it to dry.

9) The end result is a pattern of spots called a chromatogram.

shallow solvent

The point the solvent has reached as it moves up the paper is the solvent front.

Chromatography **Separates** the Parts of a Mixture

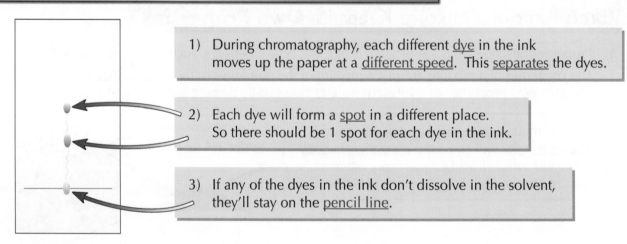

1) During chromatography, each different dye in the ink moves up the paper at a different speed. This separates the dyes.

2) Each dye will form a spot in a different place. So there should be 1 spot for each dye in the ink.

3) If any of the dyes in the ink don't dissolve in the solvent, they'll stay on the pencil line.

PRACTICAL TIP

Chromatography separates the different dyes in inks

Make sure you use a pencil to draw your baseline on the sheet of paper for your chromatogram. If you use a pen, all the components of the ink in the pen will get separated, along with the substance you're analysing, which will make your results very confusing.

Filtration and Crystallisation

Filtration and crystallisation are <u>methods</u> of <u>separating mixtures</u>. Chemists use these methods all the time to separate <u>solids</u> from <u>liquids</u>, so it's worth making sure you know how to do them.

Filtration Separates **Insoluble Solids** from **Liquids**

<u>Filtration</u> can be used to <u>separate</u> an <u>insoluble solid</u> from a <u>liquid reaction mixture</u> (insoluble solids <u>can't</u> be dissolved in the liquid). This can help make substances <u>pure</u>.

1) Put some <u>filter paper</u> in a <u>funnel</u>.
2) <u>Pour</u> the mixture into the filter paper.
3) Make sure the mixture <u>doesn't</u> go above the filter paper.
4) The <u>liquid passes through</u> the paper into the beaker. The <u>solid is left</u> behind in the filter paper.

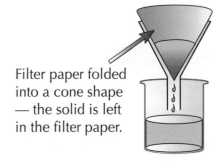

Filter paper folded into a cone shape — the solid is left in the filter paper.

Two Ways to Separate **Soluble Solids** from **Solutions**

If a solid can be <u>dissolved</u> we say it's <u>soluble</u>. There are <u>two</u> methods you can use to separate a soluble salt from a solution — <u>evaporation</u> and <u>crystallisation</u>.

Evaporation

1) Slowly <u>heat</u> the solution in an <u>evaporating dish</u>. The <u>solvent</u> will evaporate.
2) Eventually, <u>crystals</u> will start to form.
3) Keep heating until all you have left are <u>dry crystals</u>.

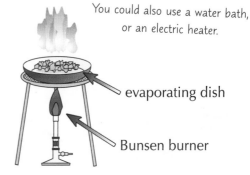

You could also use a water bath, or an electric heater.

evaporating dish

Bunsen burner

Evaporation is a really <u>quick</u> way of separating a soluble salt from a solution. But, you can only use it if the salt <u>doesn't</u> break down when it's heated. Otherwise, you'll have to use <u>crystallisation</u>.

Crystallisation

1) Gently <u>heat</u> the solution in an <u>evaporating dish</u>. Some of the <u>solvent</u> will evaporate.
2) Once some of the solvent has evaporated, <u>or</u> when you see crystals start to form, stop heating. Leave the solution to <u>cool</u>.
3) The salt should start to form <u>crystals</u>.
4) <u>Filter</u> the crystals out of the solution. Leave them in a warm place to <u>dry</u>.

You should also use crystallisation if you want to make nice big crystals of your salt.

Salt crystallising out of solution.

Remember — soluble solids will dissolve in a solvent...

...but insoluble solids <u>won't</u>. The method you use to separate a solid from a solution depends on whether it's soluble or insoluble, so make sure you know the <u>difference</u> between the two.

28

 **PRACTICAL** # Filtration and Crystallisation

Here's how you can put filtration and crystallisation to <u>good use</u>. Separating rock salt...

Filtration and Crystallisation can be Used to Separate Rock Salt

1) <u>Rock salt</u> is a <u>mixture</u> of <u>salt</u> and <u>sand</u>. <u>Salt dissolves</u> in water and <u>sand doesn't</u>.

2) This <u>difference</u> in <u>physical properties</u> means we can <u>separate</u> them. Here's what to do...

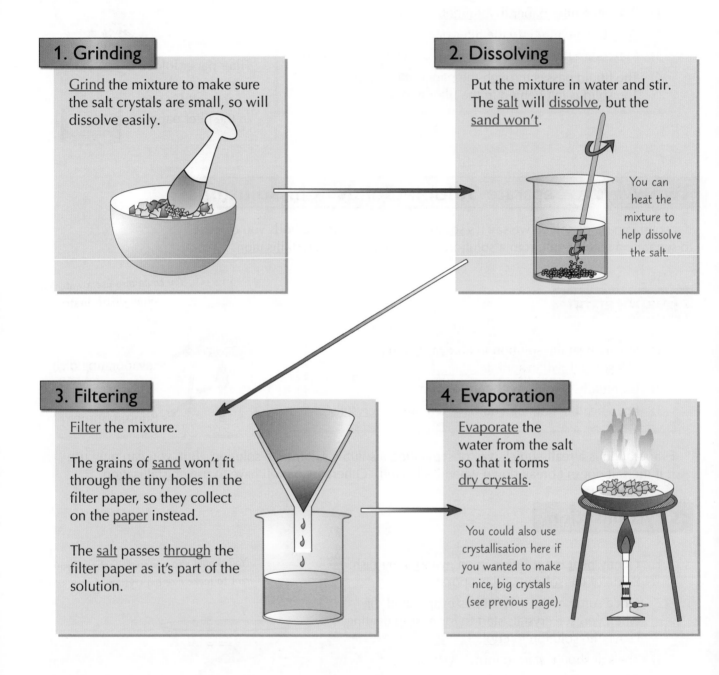

1. Grinding

<u>Grind</u> the mixture to make sure the salt crystals are small, so will dissolve easily.

2. Dissolving

Put the mixture in water and stir. The <u>salt</u> will <u>dissolve</u>, but the <u>sand won't</u>.

You can heat the mixture to help dissolve the salt.

3. Filtering

<u>Filter</u> the mixture.

The grains of <u>sand</u> won't fit through the tiny holes in the filter paper, so they collect on the <u>paper</u> instead.

The <u>salt</u> passes <u>through</u> the filter paper as it's part of the solution.

4. Evaporation

<u>Evaporate</u> the water from the salt so that it forms <u>dry crystals</u>.

You could also use crystallisation here if you wanted to make nice, big crystals (see previous page).

 EXAM TIP ### Separating rock salt requires filtration and evaporation

You may be asked how to separate <u>another type of mixture</u> containing <u>insoluble</u> and <u>soluble</u> solids — just apply the <u>same method</u> and <u>think through</u> what is happening in each stage.

Topic 1 — Atomic Structure and the Periodic Table

Simple Distillation

Distillation is used to separate mixtures which contain liquids. This first page looks at simple distillation.

Simple Distillation is Used to Separate Solutions

1) Simple distillation is used to separate a liquid from a solution.
2) First, the solution is heated.
3) The part of the solution that has the lowest boiling point evaporates first and turns into a gas.
4) The gas travels into the condenser.
5) In the condenser, the gas is cooled and condenses (turns back into a liquid).
6) The liquid drips out of the condenser and can be collected.
7) The rest of the solution is left behind in the flask.

> You can use simple distillation to get pure water from seawater.
> The water evaporates. It is then condensed and collected.
> This leaves the salt behind in the flask.

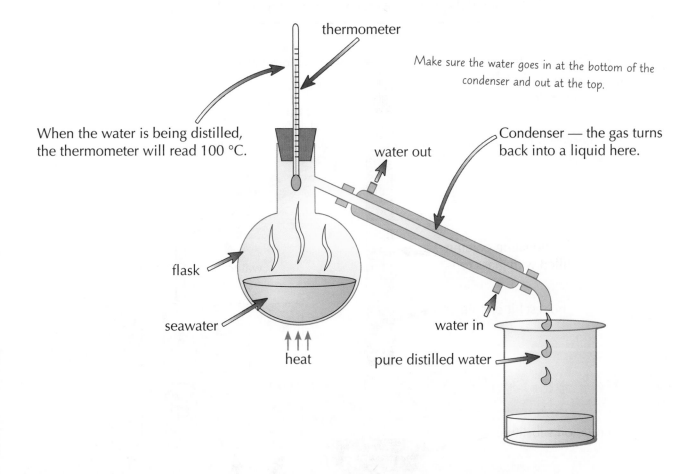

thermometer

Make sure the water goes in at the bottom of the condenser and out at the top.

When the water is being distilled, the thermometer will read 100 °C.

water out

Condenser — the gas turns back into a liquid here.

flask

seawater

heat

water in

pure distilled water

8) Simple distillation can't be used to separate mixtures of liquids with similar boiling points. So, you need to use another method instead — like fractional distillation (see next page).

PRACTICAL TIP

Only gas should leave the flask during simple distillation

Make sure you don't put too much liquid in the flask, or heat it too vigorously — some of the unseparated solution could get into the condenser, meaning your product won't be pure.

Fractional Distillation

Another type of distillation is <u>fractional distillation</u>. This is trickier to carry out than simple distillation, but it can separate out <u>mixtures of liquids</u> even if their <u>boiling points</u> are close together.

Fractional Distillation is Used to Separate a **Mixture of Liquids**

1) If you've got a <u>mixture of liquids</u> you can separate it using <u>fractional distillation</u>.
2) You put your <u>mixture</u> in a flask and stick a <u>fractionating column</u> on top, as shown below. Then you heat it.
3) The <u>different liquids</u> will have <u>different boiling points</u>.
4) So, they will evaporate at <u>different temperatures</u>.
5) The substance with the <u>lowest boiling point</u> evaporates first.
6) When the temperature on the thermometer matches the boiling point of this substance, it will reach the <u>top</u> of the column.
7) The substance will then enter the condenser, where it cools and <u>condenses</u>.
8) You can <u>collect</u> the liquid as it drips out of the condenser.
9) When the first liquid has been collected, you <u>raise</u> the <u>temperature</u> until the <u>next one</u> reaches the top.

The diagram shows an experiment that can be used to show how fractional distillation of <u>crude oil</u> at a refinery works (see p.110).

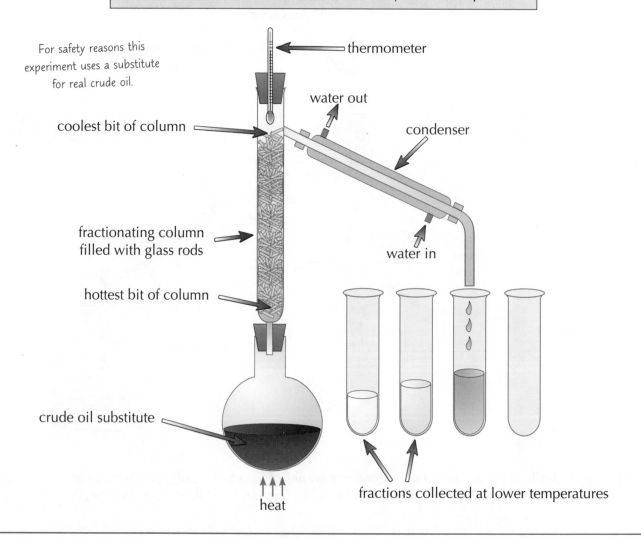

For safety reasons this experiment uses a substitute for real crude oil.

thermometer

coolest bit of column

water out

condenser

fractionating column filled with glass rods

water in

hottest bit of column

crude oil substitute

heat

fractions collected at lower temperatures

Fractional distillation is used in the lab and industry

You've made it to the end of the pages on <u>separation techniques</u>, so make sure you understand what each of the methods can be used to separate and the <u>apparatus</u> set-up for each technique.

Warm-Up & Exam Questions

So the last few pages have all been about mixtures and how to separate them. Here are some questions to get stuck into and make sure you know your filtration from your distillation...

Warm-Up Questions

1) True or False? The chemical properties of a substance are changed by it being part of a mixture.
2) Give the name of a method to separate a soluble solid from a solution.
3) Which part of the fractionating column is coolest during fractional distillation?

Exam Questions

1 A scientist is using paper chromatography to compare two different compounds. He draws a pencil line near the bottom of a sheet of filter paper and adds a spot of each of the different compounds to the line, leaving gaps between each spot.

1.1 Describe the next thing that the scientist should do with the filter paper.

[1 mark]

1.2 Why is pencil used to draw the line on the filter paper?

[1 mark]

2 A gardener uses a mixture of insoluble sharp sand and soluble ammonium sulfate fertiliser to treat his lawn.

A student plans to use the method below to separate the gardener's mixture into sharp sand and ammonium sulfate.

1. Mix the lawn sand with water and stir.
2. Filter the mixture using filter paper.
3. Pour the remaining solution into an evaporating dish and slowly heat it.

Explain the purpose of **each** of the steps in the student's method.

[3 marks]

3 Simple distillation can be used to separate mixtures of liquids. **Table 1** gives the boiling points of three liquids.

Figure 1

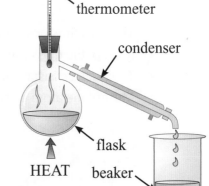

Table 1

Liquid	Boiling point (°C)
Methanoic acid	101
Propanone	56
Water	100

3.1 **Figure 1** shows the apparatus needed for simple distillation. Describe how the apparatus shown in **Figure 1** could be used to separate propanone from a solution of propanone and water. Propanone is highly flammable. Include any relevant safety precautions in your answer.

[6 marks]

3.2 Simple distillation can **not** be used to separate water from a solution of water and methanoic acid. Give a technique that **would** be suitable for separating water and methanoic acid.

[1 mark]

The History of the Atom

You may have thought you were done with the <u>atom</u> after page 17. Unfortunately, you don't get away that easily. The next couple of pages are all about how <u>scientists</u> came to understand the atom as we do today.

Ideas About What Atoms Look Like Have Changed Over Time

1) Scientists used to think that atoms were <u>solid spheres</u>.

2) They then found atoms contain even smaller, negatively charged particles — <u>electrons</u>.

3) This led to a model called the '<u>plum pudding model</u>' being created.

4) The plum pudding model showed the atom as a <u>ball</u> of <u>positive charge</u> with <u>electrons scattered</u> in this ball.

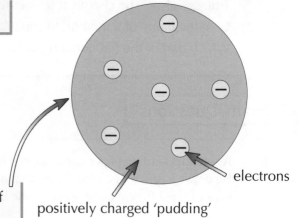

electrons

positively charged 'pudding'

Experiments Showed that the Plum Pudding Model Was Wrong

1) Later, scientists carried out <u>alpha particle scattering experiments</u>. They fired positively charged <u>alpha particles</u> at a very thin sheet of gold.

2) From the plum pudding model, they <u>expected</u> most of the particles to <u>go straight through</u> the sheet. They predicted that a few particles would <u>change direction</u> by a <u>small</u> amount.

3) But instead, some particles changed direction <u>more than expected</u>. A small number even went <u>backwards</u>.

4) This meant the plum pudding model <u>couldn't</u> be right.

5) So, scientists came up with the <u>nuclear model</u> of the atom:

- There's a tiny, positively charged <u>nucleus</u> at the centre of the atom.
- Most of the <u>mass</u> is in the nucleus.
- The nucleus is surrounded by 'cloud' of negative <u>electrons</u>.
- Most of the atom is <u>empty space</u>.

A few particles go backwards.

Most of the particles pass through empty space, but a few change direction.

The History of the Atom

Bohr's **Nuclear Model** Explains a Lot

1) <u>Niels Bohr</u> changed the nuclear model of the atom.
   (See previous page for more information on the nuclear model).

2) He suggested that the electrons <u>orbit</u> (go around) the nucleus in <u>shells</u> (levels).

3) Each shell is a <u>fixed distance</u> from the nucleus.

4) Bohr's theory was supported by many <u>experiments</u>.
   Experiments later showed that Bohr's theory was correct.

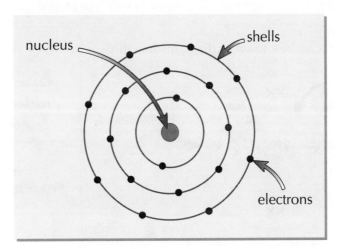

Later Experiments Found **Protons** and **Neutrons**

1) More experiments by scientists showed that the nucleus can be <u>divided</u> into smaller particles.
   Each particle has the <u>same positive charge</u>. These particles were named <u>protons</u>.

2) Experiments by <u>James Chadwick</u> showed that the nucleus also contained <u>neutral particles</u> — <u>neutrons</u>.
   This happened about 20 years after scientists agreed that atoms have nuclei.

3) This led to a model of the atom which was <u>pretty close</u> to the one we have today (see page 17).

Our understanding of what an atom looks like has changed

The history of the atom is a fine example of the scientific method. It shows how our understanding of science can go through <u>many stages</u>, as scientists built upon other people's work with <u>new evidence</u>. And new evidence allows <u>new predictions</u> to be made, so the progress <u>continues</u>.

Electronic Structure

Electrons don't just float around the nucleus randomly. They move in areas called shells.

Electron Shell Rules:

1) Electrons always move in shells (sometimes called energy levels).
2) The inner shells are always filled up first. These are the ones closest to the nucleus.
3) Only a certain number of electrons are allowed in each shell:

1st shell: 2   2nd shell: 8   3rd shell: 8

4) Atoms are a lot more stable when they have full electron shells.
5) In most atoms, the outer shell is not full. These atoms will react to fill it.

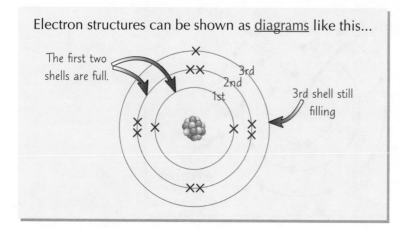

Electron structures can be shown as diagrams like this...

...or as numbers like this: 2, 8, 1

number of electrons in 1st shell
number of electrons in 2nd shell
number of electrons in 3rd shell

Both of these show the electron structure of sodium.

Follow the Rules to Work Out Electronic Structures

You can easily work out the electronic structures for the first 20 elements of the periodic table (things get a bit more complicated after that).

EXAMPLE: What is the electronic structure of magnesium?

1) From the periodic table, you can see that magnesium's atomic number is 12. This means it has 12 protons. So it must have 12 electrons.
2) Follow the 'Electron Shell Rules' above. The first shell can only take 2 electrons.   2...
3) The second shell can take up to 8 electrons.   2, 8...
4) So far we have a total of 10 electrons (2 + 8). So the third shell must also be partly filled with 2 electrons. This makes 12 electrons in total (2 + 8 + 2).

So the electronic structure for magnesium must be 2, 8, 2.

Here are some more examples of electronic structures:

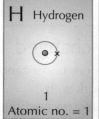
H Hydrogen
1
Atomic no. = 1

He Helium
2
Atomic no. = 2

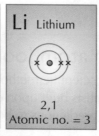
Li Lithium
2,1
Atomic no. = 3

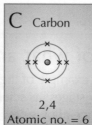
C Carbon
2,4
Atomic no. = 6

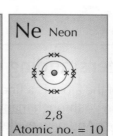
Ne Neon
2,8
Atomic no. = 10

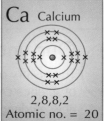
Ca Calcium
2,8,8,2
Atomic no. = 20

Topic 1 — Atomic Structure and the Periodic Table

Development of the Periodic Table

We haven't always known as much about chemistry as we do now.
Early chemists looked at <u>patterns</u> in the elements' properties to help them understand chemistry better.

In the **Early 1800s** Elements Were **Arranged** By **Atomic Mass**

1) Until quite recently, scientists hadn't discovered protons, neutrons or electrons.
   So they had <u>no idea</u> of <u>atomic number</u>.

2) So scientists used <u>relative atomic mass</u> to arrange the elements into a <u>periodic table</u>.

3) These early periodic tables were <u>not complete</u>.

4) This is because <u>not all</u> of the elements had been <u>found</u> yet.

Remember — the relative atomic mass is the average mass of one atom of an element.

5) And putting the elements in order of atomic mass meant that
   some elements were also put in the <u>wrong group</u> (column).

Dmitri Mendeleev Left Gaps and **Predicted** New Elements

1) In <u>1869</u>, a scientist called <u>Mendeleev</u> took all of the known elements and arranged them into a table.

<u>Mendeleev's Table of the Elements</u>

```
H
Li  Be                                               B   C   N   O   F
Na  Mg                                               Al  Si  P   S   Cl
K   Ca  *   Ti  V   Cr  Mn  Fe  Co  Ni  Cu  Zn  *   *   As  Se  Br
Rb  Sr  Y   Zr  Nb  Mo  *   Ru  Rh  Pd  Ag  Cd  In  Sn  Sb  Te  I
Cs  Ba  *   *   Ta  W   *   Os  Ir  Pt  Au  Hg  Tl  Pb  Bi
```

2) He ordered them <u>mainly</u> by their <u>atomic mass</u>.

3) Sometimes he <u>switched</u> their positions or left <u>gaps</u> in the table.

4) This was so he could make sure that elements with <u>similar properties</u> stayed in the <u>same groups</u>.

5) Some of the <u>gaps</u> left space for elements that hadn't been found yet.
   Mendeleev used the position of the gaps to <u>predict the properties</u> of these elements.

6) <u>New elements</u> have been found since which <u>fit</u> into these gaps.
   This shows that Mendeleev's ideas were right.

- <u>Isotopes</u> were discovered a while after Mendeleev made his Table of Elements.
- Isotopes have different atomic masses but share the same properties.
  This means they have the <u>same position</u> on the periodic table.
- So, Mendeleev was <u>right</u> to swap some elements around to keep properties together
  — even if it meant they weren't in order of atomic mass.

By leaving gaps in the table Mendeleev had the right idea

Make sure you can <u>describe</u> what Mendeleev did to <u>fix the problems</u> with early periodic tables.

The Modern Periodic Table

Mendeleev got pretty close to producing something that you might <u>recognise</u> as a periodic table. The big breakthrough came when the <u>structure</u> of the <u>atom</u> was understood a bit better.

The Periodic Table Helps you to See Patterns in Properties

1) There are about <u>100 elements</u>.

2) In the periodic table the elements are laid out in order of <u>increasing atomic number</u>.

3) There are <u>repeating (periodic) patterns</u> in the <u>properties</u> of the elements.
These periodic properties give the periodic table its name.

4) <u>Metals</u> are found to the <u>left</u> of the periodic table and <u>non-metals</u> are found to the <u>right</u>.

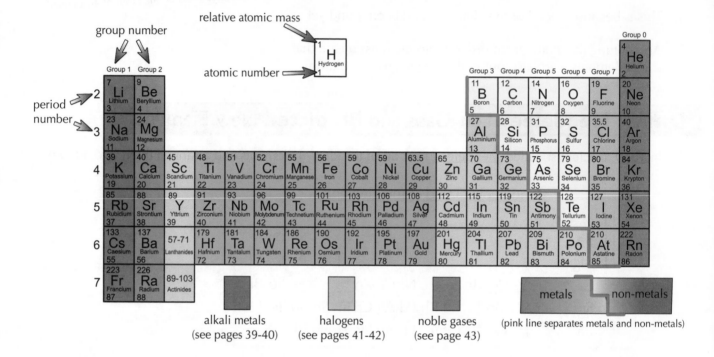

alkali metals
(see pages 39-40)

halogens
(see pages 41-42)

noble gases
(see page 43)

(pink line separates metals and non-metals)

5) Elements with <u>similar properties</u> are arranged to form <u>columns</u>. These <u>columns</u> are called <u>groups</u>.

6) The <u>group number</u> of an element is the <u>same</u> as the number of <u>outer shell electrons</u> it has.
(Except for <u>Group 0</u> — helium has two electrons in its outer shell and the rest have eight.)

7) So, all the elements in a group have the <u>same</u> number of electrons in their outer shell.
This means that elements in a group <u>react</u> in <u>similar ways</u>.

> • The <u>Group 1</u> elements are Li, Na, K, Rb, Cs and Fr.
> • They all have <u>one</u> electron in their outer shells.
> • They're all <u>metals</u> and they <u>react in a similar way</u>.

See pages 39-40 for more on Group 1 elements.

8) If you know the <u>properties</u> of <u>one element</u>, you can <u>predict</u> properties of <u>other elements</u> in that group.

9) You can also make predictions about trends in <u>reactivity</u>.
E.g. in Group 1, the elements react <u>more violently</u> as you go <u>down</u> the group.

10) The <u>rows</u> in the periodic table are called <u>periods</u>. Each new period represents another <u>shell</u> of electrons.

The periodic table really helps with understanding chemistry

The periodic table is organised into <u>groups</u> and <u>periods</u>. This lets you see <u>patterns in reactivity</u> <u>and properties</u>. And this means you can make <u>predictions</u> on how reactions will occur.

Warm-Up & Exam Questions

The last few pages have been tough with lots of information to learn. Luckily, here are some questions to get your head around to help you test your understanding.

Warm-Up Questions

1) Describe the 'plum pudding' model of the atom.
2) How many electrons can be held in the following:
   a) the first shell of an atom?
   b) the second shell of an atom?
3) Why did Mendeleev leave gaps in his table of the elements?

Exam Questions

1 The periodic table contains all the known elements arranged in order. **(Grade 3-4)**

1.1 How were elements generally ordered in early periodic tables?
Tick **one** box.

☐ alphabetically ☐ by atomic number ☐ by abundance ☐ by atomic mass

[1 mark]

1.2 How are the elements arranged in the modern periodic table?
Tick **one** box.

☐ alphabetically ☐ by atomic number ☐ by abundance ☐ by atomic mass

[1 mark]

1.3 Explain why elements in the same group of the periodic table have similar chemical properties.

[1 mark]

2 The atomic number of sulfur is 16. **(Grade 4-5)**

2.1 Complete **Figure 1** to show the electronic structure of sulfur.

Figure 1

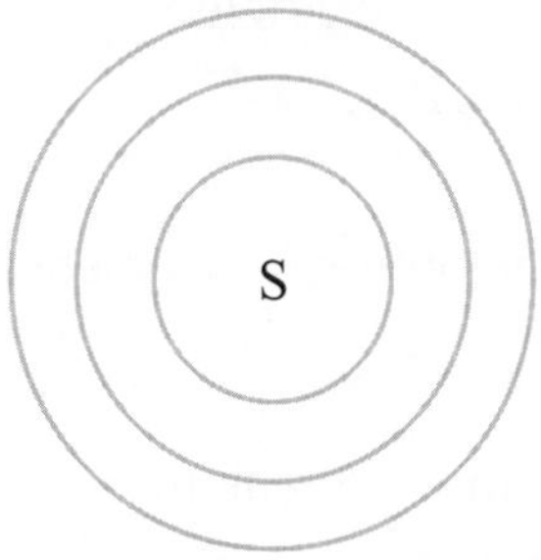

[1 mark]

2.2 Which group of the periodic table is sulfur in?

[1 mark]

2.3 Name another element that has the same number of electrons in its outer shell as sulfur.

[1 mark]

2.4 How many electrons does sulfur need to gain to have a full outer shell?

[1 mark]

Metals and Non-Metals

Metals are used for all sorts of things so they're <u>really important</u> in modern life.

Most Elements are **Metals**

1) Metals are elements which can <u>form positive ions</u> when they react.
2) They're towards the <u>bottom</u> and to the <u>left</u> of the periodic table.
3) <u>Most elements</u> in the periodic table are metals.
4) <u>Non-metals</u> are at the far <u>right</u> and <u>top</u> of the periodic table.
5) Non-metals <u>don't</u> usually <u>form positive ions</u> when they react.

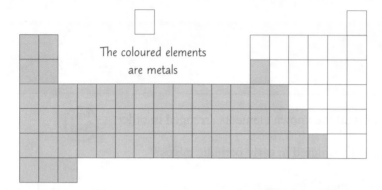

The coloured elements are metals

Only the white elements are non-metals.

The **Electronic Structure** of Atoms Affects How They Will React

1) Atoms are more <u>stable</u> with a full outer shell. So, they react by <u>losing</u>, <u>gaining</u> or <u>sharing</u> electrons.
2) Metal elements are to the <u>left</u> and towards the <u>bottom</u> of the periodic table so they lose electrons quite easily. When this happens, they <u>form positive ions</u>, with a full outer shell.
3) <u>Non-metals</u> are to the right of the periodic table or towards the top, so it's easier for them to <u>share</u> or <u>gain</u> electrons to get a full outer shell.

Metals and **Non-Metals** Have **Different Physical Properties**

1) All metals have <u>similar</u> physical properties.

- They're <u>strong</u> (hard to break), but can be <u>bent</u> or <u>hammered</u> into different shapes (malleable).
- They're great at <u>conducting heat</u> and <u>electricity</u>.
- They have high <u>boiling and melting points</u>.

2) Non-metals <u>don't</u> tend to show the same properties as metals.

- They tend to be <u>dull looking</u>.
- They're more <u>brittle</u>. This means they'll <u>break</u> more easily if you try to <u>bend</u> them.
- They're <u>not always solids</u> at room temperature.
- They <u>don't</u> usually <u>conduct electricity</u>.
- They often have a <u>lower density</u>.

Metals have quite different properties from non-metals

And you'll need to make sure you can remember them. Try <u>covering up</u> the lists of properties of metals and non-metals above and <u>writing down</u> as many as you can from memory.

Group 1 Elements

Group 1 elements are known as the alkali metals. As metals go, they're pretty reactive.

The Group 1 Elements are Reactive, Soft Metals

1) The alkali metals are lithium, sodium, potassium, rubidium, caesium and francium.

2) They all have one electron in their outer shell.
This makes them very reactive. It also gives them similar properties.

3) The alkali metals are all soft.

4) They all have low density (they're quite light).

There are Patterns in the Properties of Group 1 Metals

1) As you go down Group 1, the properties of the alkali metals change.
For example:

- Reactivity increases — the outer electron is more easily lost as it gets further from the nucleus. This is because it's less attracted to the nucleus.

- Melting and boiling points get lower.

- Relative atomic mass goes up.

Group 1	Group 2
7 Li Lithium 3	
23 Na Sodium 11	
39 K Potassium 19	
85.5 Rb Rubidium 37	
133 Cs Caesium 55	
223 Fr Francium 87	

2) These patterns in the properties are called trends.

The properties of Group 1 metals change as you go down the group

In the exam you might be given a trend and then asked to predict properties of other Group 1 metals. For example, the reactivity of Group 1 metals increases as you go down the group, so you know that potassium will react more vigorously than sodium.

Group 1 Elements

You met Group 1 metals on the previous page, so now it's time to learn about some of their reactions...

Alkali Metals Form Ionic Compounds with Non-Metals

The Group 1 elements easily lose their one outer electron to form a full outer shell.
So they form 1+ ions easily.

Reaction With Water

1) The reactions are vigorous and produce a metal hydroxide and hydrogen gas:

alkali metal + water → metal hydroxide + hydrogen

For example:

sodium + water → sodium hydroxide + hydrogen
$$2Na_{(s)} + 2H_2O_{(l)} \rightarrow 2NaOH_{(aq)} + H_{2(g)}$$

2) The metal hydroxides are salts that dissolve in the water.

The little letters in brackets after each substance in the reaction show what state the substance is in — see p.64.

3) The more reactive (lower down in the group) an alkali metal is, the more violent the reaction.

4) Lithium, sodium and potassium float and move around the surface, fizzing furiously.

5) The reaction with potassium gives out enough energy to ignite the hydrogen (set it on fire).

Reaction With Chlorine

1) Group 1 metals react vigorously when heated in chlorine gas to form white salts called metal chlorides.

alkali metal + chlorine → metal chloride

For example:

sodium + chlorine → sodium chloride
$$2Na_{(s)} + Cl_{2(g)} \rightarrow 2NaCl_{(s)}$$

2) As you go down the group, the reaction gets more vigorous.

Reaction With Oxygen

1) Group 1 metals can react with oxygen to form a metal oxide.

2) Different types of oxide will form depending on the Group 1 metal.

3) Group 1 metals are shiny but when they react with oxygen in the air they turn a dull grey (they tarnish). This is because a layer of metal oxide is formed on the surface.

Alkali metals all react in a similar way...

...which is handy for you, because it means you don't need to learn the reaction products for each metal separately. You just need to remember the types of product that are formed during each reaction, then switch 'metal' for whichever Group 1 element you're interested in.

Group 7 Elements

The Group 7 elements are known as the halogens. Like the alkali metals, halogens also show trends down the group. However, these trends are a bit different...

The Halogens Show Patterns in their Properties

1) The halogens are fluorine, chlorine, bromine, iodine and astatine.

2) As elements, the halogens form molecules that contain two atoms.
   For example, chlorine (Cl_2) is a fairly reactive, poisonous green gas.

3) As you go down Group 7, the halogens:

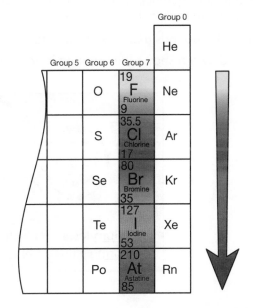

- become less reactive — it's harder to gain an extra electron as the outer shell is further from the nucleus.

- have higher melting and boiling points.

- have higher relative atomic masses.

You can use these trends to predict properties of halogens. E.g. iodine will have a higher boiling point than chlorine as it's further down the group.

4) All the Group 7 elements react in similar ways.
   This is because they all have seven electrons in their outer shell.

Halogens can Form Molecular Compounds

1) When halogen atoms react with other non-metals, they share electrons and form covalent bonds (see page 53). This is so they can get a full outer shell.

2) These reactions form compounds with simple molecular structures (see p.54-55).

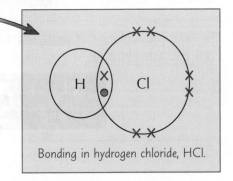

Bonding in hydrogen chloride, HCl.

Halogens all exist as molecules with two atoms

Just like alkali metals, you may be asked to predict the properties of a halogen from a given trend down the group. Make sure you understand why the halogens' electronic structures mean they react in similar ways.

Group 7 Elements

You also need to know all about how the halogens <u>react</u> with <u>metals</u> and <u>halide salts</u>, so get reading this page...

Halogens Form **Ionic Bonds** with **Metals**

1) The halogens form <u>1– ions</u> called <u>halides</u>:

- <u>fluoride</u>, F^-
- <u>bromide</u>, Br^-
- <u>chloride</u>, Cl^-
- <u>iodide</u>, I^-

2) Halides form when halogens bond with <u>metals</u>.
For example Na^+Cl^- or $Ca^{2+}Br^-_2$.

3) The compounds (halide salts) that form have <u>ionic structures</u>.

4) The diagram shows the bonding in sodium chloride, NaCl.

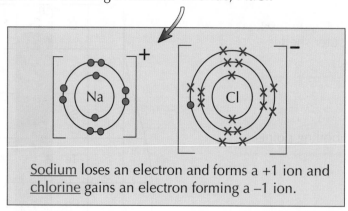

Sodium loses an electron and forms a +1 ion and chlorine gains an electron forming a –1 ion.

More Reactive Halogens **Displace Less Reactive** Halogens

1) A reaction can take place between a <u>halogen</u> and the <u>halide salt</u> of a <u>less reactive</u> halogen.

2) These are called <u>displacement reactions</u>.

3) When this happens, the <u>less reactive</u> halogen changes from a halide (1– ion) to a <u>halogen</u>.
The <u>more reactive</u> halogen changes from a halogen into a <u>halide ion</u> and becomes part of the <u>salt</u>.

For example, chlorine is <u>more reactive</u> than bromine.
So if you add <u>chlorine</u> to a solution containing a <u>bromide salt</u>, bromine will be <u>displaced</u>.

$$Cl_{2(g)} \ + \ 2KBr_{(aq)} \ \rightarrow \ Br_{2(aq)} \ + \ 2KCl_{(aq)}$$
Pale green   Orange

Halogens higher up the group will displace the ones lower down

The halogens get <u>less reactive</u> as you go down the group. So a halogen will only be able to displace another halogen if it's <u>higher up</u> in Group 7. If it's lower down Group 7, <u>no reaction</u> will happen.

Group 0 Elements

The <u>noble gases don't react</u> with very much and you can't even see them — makes them a bit <u>dull</u> really.

Group 0 Elements are All **Unreactive, Colourless Gases**

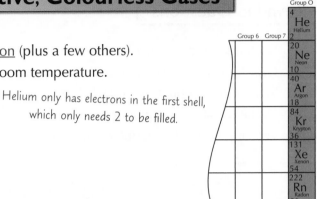

1) Group 0 elements are called the <u>noble gases</u>.
   They include the elements <u>helium</u>, <u>neon</u> and <u>argon</u> (plus a few others).

2) All elements in Group 0 are <u>colourless gases</u> at room temperature.

3) They all have <u>eight outer shell electrons</u>, apart from helium which has two.
   This means they have a <u>stable full outer shell</u>.

   Helium only has electrons in the first shell, which only needs 2 to be filled.

4) This stability makes them very <u>unreactive</u> (<u>inert</u>).
   This means they don't form molecules easily.
   So the elements are <u>single atoms</u>.

5) Because noble gases are unreactive, some reactions are carried out in an <u>atmosphere</u> that <u>only</u> contains a noble gas, instead of air.

6) This is done if the <u>reactants</u> could react with things in the <u>air</u> (e.g. oxygen or water) instead of taking part in the reaction you're trying to do. It's also done if the <u>products</u> react with things in the air.

There are **Patterns** in the **Properties** of the Noble Gases

1) As you go down Group 0, the <u>relative atomic masses</u> of the elements <u>increase</u>.

2) This means that as you go down the group, the elements have <u>more electrons</u>.

3) More electrons means <u>stronger forces</u> between atoms.

4) The stronger the forces, the <u>higher</u> the <u>boiling point</u>.
   So as you go down Group 0, the boiling points <u>increase</u>.

5) If you're given the boiling point of one noble gas you can <u>predict</u> the boiling point for <u>another one</u>.
   So make sure you know the <u>pattern</u>.

Noble Gas
helium
neon
argon
krypton
xenon
radon

Increasing boiling point

EXAMPLE: **Neon is a gas at 25 °C. Predict what state helium is at this temperature.**

Helium has a lower boiling point than neon as it is further up the group.

So, helium must also be a gas at 25 °C.

EXAMPLE: **Radon has a boiling point of –62 °C and krypton has a boiling point of –153 °C. Predict the boiling point of xenon.**

Xenon comes in between radon and krypton in the group.
So, you can predict that its boiling point would be between their boiling points.
E.g. xenon has a boiling point of –100 °C.

The actual boiling point of xenon is –108 °C — which is between –62 °C and –153 °C. Just as predicted.

Just like other groups of elements, the noble gases follow patterns...

Although they're <u>unreactive</u> and <u>hard to see</u>, they're actually pretty useful. It took a while to discover them, but we now know all about them, including the trend in their boiling points.

Warm-Up & Exam Questions

These questions are all about the groups of the periodic table that you need to know about. Treat the exam questions like the real thing — don't look back through the book until you've finished.

Warm-Up Questions

1) Do metals form positive or negative ions?
2) Give two physical properties of most metals.
3) What is the product formed when lithium reacts with chlorine?
4) Do halide ions have a positive or a negative charge?
5) Which group of the periodic table are the noble gases in?

Exam Questions

1   **Table 1** shows some of the physical properties of four of the halogens. Grade 1-3

Table 1

Halogen	Physical state at room temperature
Fluorine	gas
Chlorine	gas
Bromine	liquid
Iodine	solid

1.1   Which halogen in **Table 1** is the most reactive?

[1 mark]

1.2   Which halogen in **Table 1** has the highest melting point?

[1 mark]

2   **Figure 1** shows the periodic table. Grade 3-4

Figure 1

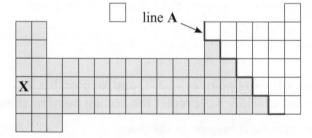

2.1   Element **X** is found in the first column of the periodic table.
What name is given to the elements found in the first column of the periodic table?
Tick **one** box.

| | halogens | | alkali metals | | noble gases | | non-metals |

[1 mark]

2.2   Element **Y** does not conduct electricity.
Predict whether element **Y** will be found to the left or the right of line **A** in **Figure 1**.
Explain your answer.

[2 marks]

Exam Questions

3 Group 1 elements include lithium, sodium and potassium.

3.1 Explain why the Group 1 elements react vigorously with water.

[1 mark]

3.2 The equation for the reaction of potassium with water is:

$$2K + 2H_2O \rightarrow 2KOH + H_2$$

Name the **two** products of the reaction.

[2 marks]

3.3 Potassium is more reactive than lithium and sodium.
Why do the Group 1 elements become more reactive as you go down Group 1?
Tick **one** box.

☐ The outer electron is closer to the nucleus and so more attracted to the nucleus.

☐ The outer electron is closer to the nucleus and so less attracted to the nucleus.

☐ The outer electron is further from the nucleus and so less attracted to the nucleus.

☐ The outer electron is further from the nucleus and so more attracted to the nucleus.

[1 mark]

4 Chlorine is a Group 7 element.
Chlorine's electron arrangement is shown in **Figure 2**.

Figure 2

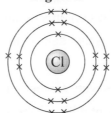

4.1 Chlorine is very reactive and forms compounds with metals.
What type of bonds form between chlorine and metals?

[1 mark]

When chlorine is bubbled through potassium iodide solution a reaction occurs.
The equation below shows the reaction.

$$Cl_{2(g)} + 2KI_{(aq)} \rightarrow I_{2(aq)} + 2KCl_{(aq)}$$

4.2 Identify the type of reaction that occurs.

[1 mark]

4.3 What does the reaction show about the relative reactivities of Cl_2 and I_2? Give a reason for your answer.

[2 marks]

4.4 None of the elements in Group 0 will react with potassium iodide or potassium bromide.
Using your knowledge of the electronic structure of the Group 0 elements,
explain why no reaction occurs.

[1 mark]

Topic 1 — Atomic Structure and the Periodic Table

Revision Summary for Topic 1

<u>Topic 1</u> — finished. But hold on there, don't rush on to Topic 2 just yet.
There's one more thing for you to do...

* Try these questions and <u>tick off each one</u> when you <u>get it right</u>.
* When you've done <u>all the questions</u> under a heading and are <u>completely happy</u> with it, tick it off.

Atoms, Elements and Compounds (p.17-22) ☑

1) Draw an atom. Label the nucleus and the electrons. ☑
2) What is the relative mass of a neutron? ☑
3) What is the smallest part of an element that you can have? ☑
4) Give the formula for:
   a) Carbon dioxide   b) Water ☑
5) Balance these equations:
   a) $Mg + O_2 \rightarrow MgO$ b) $H_2SO_4 + NaOH \rightarrow Na_2SO_4 + H_2O$ ☑

Mixtures and Separation (p.25-30) ☑

6) Are there any chemical bonds between the different parts of a mixture? ☑
7) What method could you use to separate dyes in an ink? ☑
8) What is the name of the pattern formed from carrying out paper chromatography? ☑
9) Which method of separation is useful to separate an insoluble solid from a liquid? ☑

Electronic Structure and the History of the Periodic Table (p.32-36) ☑

10) What did scientists expect to see during the alpha particle scattering experiments? ☑
11) Which scientist first found that the nucleus contains neutrons? ☑
12) What is the maximum number of electrons that can be in the third shell of an atom? ☑
13) What is the electronic structure of sodium? ☑
14) True or false? In the early 1800s, elements were arranged in the periodic table by their abundance. ☑
15) What does the group number of an element tell you about its electrons? ☑

Groups of the Periodic Table (p.38-43) ☑

16) Where are non-metals on the periodic table? ☑
17) State two trends as you go down Group 1 of the periodic table. ☑
18) How do the boiling points of halogens change as you go down the group? ☑
19) Halogens form ions when they react with metals. What is the charge of the halogen ions? ☑
20) Chlorine is added to a solution containing a bromide salt.
    Will the chlorine displace the bromine in the solution? ☑
21) Why are the Group 0 elements single atoms? ☑
22) How do the boiling points change as you go down Group 0? ☑

Ions

Ions crop up all over the place in chemistry. You need to know <u>what</u> they are and <u>how</u> they form. Luckily for you, this page has got that covered. So crack on with it.

Ions are Made When **Electrons** are Transferred

1) <u>Ions</u> are <u>charged</u> particles — for example Cl^- or Mg^{2+}.

   Ions will always have a '+' or '−' sign after the formula. A '+' tells you the ion is positive. A '−' sign tells you the ion is negative.

2) Ions are formed when atoms <u>gain</u> or <u>lose</u> electrons.

3) They do this to get a <u>full outer shell</u> — like a noble gas. This is because a full outer shell is very <u>stable</u>.

   The noble gases are in Group O of the periodic table.

4) <u>Metal</u> atoms <u>lose</u> electrons from their <u>outer shell</u> to form <u>positive ions</u>.

5) <u>Non-metal</u> atoms <u>gain</u> electrons into their <u>outer shell</u> to form <u>negative ions</u>.

6) The <u>number</u> of electrons lost or gained is the same as the <u>charge</u> on the ion. For <u>example</u>:

> If 2 electrons are <u>lost</u>, the particle now has two more protons than electrons. So the charge is <u>2+</u>.
>
> If 3 electrons are <u>gained</u>, the particle now has three more electrons than protons. So the charge is <u>3−</u>.

Ionic Bonding — **Transfer** of Electrons

1) <u>Metals</u> and <u>non-metals</u> can react together.
2) When this happens, the <u>metal</u> atoms <u>lose</u> electrons to form <u>positively charged ions</u>.
3) The <u>non-metal atoms gain</u> these <u>electrons</u> to form <u>negatively charged ions</u>.
4) These oppositely charged ions are <u>strongly attracted</u> to one another by <u>electrostatic forces</u>.
5) This attraction is called an <u>ionic bond</u>. It holds the ions together to make an <u>ionic compound</u>.

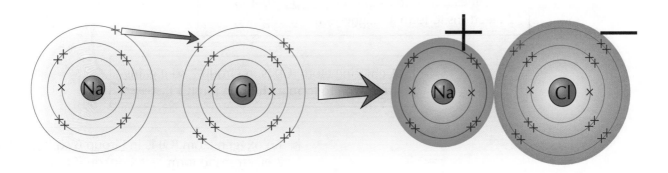

Ions

You need to be able to predict the ions that the atoms in Groups 1, 2, 6 and 7 will form.
Don't worry, though — the <u>periodic table</u> is here to help you.

You can **Work Out** What Ions are Formed by Groups **1, 2, 6 and 7**

1) <u>Group 1 and 2 elements</u> are <u>metals</u>. They <u>lose</u> electrons to form <u>positive ions</u>.

2) <u>Group 6 and 7 elements</u> are <u>non-metals</u>. They <u>gain</u> electrons to form <u>negative ions</u>.

3) Elements in the same <u>group</u> all have the same number of <u>outer electrons</u>.
   So they have to <u>lose or gain</u> the same number to get a full outer shell.
   And this means that they form ions with the <u>same charges</u>.

4) You <u>don't</u> have to <u>remember</u> what ions <u>most elements</u> form. You can just look at the periodic table.

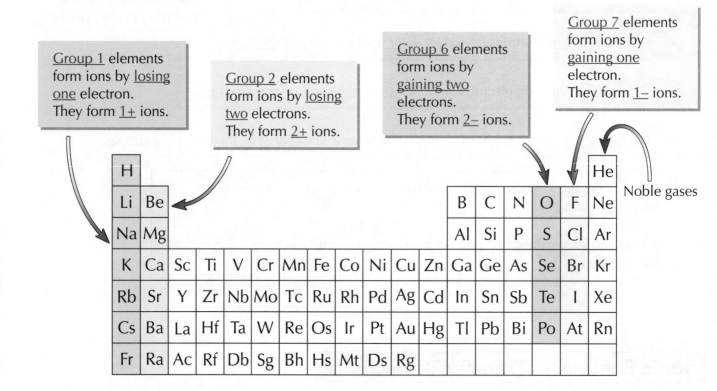

Group 1 elements form ions by <u>losing one</u> electron. They form <u>1+</u> ions.

Group 2 elements form ions by <u>losing two</u> electrons. They form <u>2+</u> ions.

Group 6 elements form ions by <u>gaining two</u> electrons. They form <u>2−</u> ions.

Group 7 elements form ions by <u>gaining one</u> electron. They form <u>1−</u> ions.

Noble gases

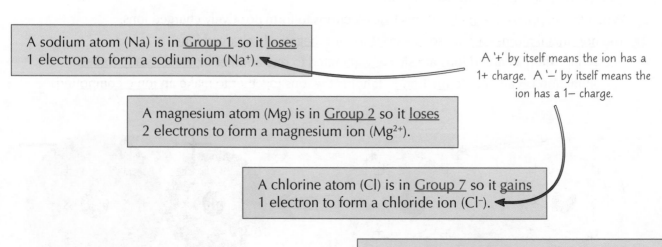

A sodium atom (Na) is in <u>Group 1</u> so it <u>loses</u> 1 electron to form a sodium ion (Na^+).

A magnesium atom (Mg) is in <u>Group 2</u> so it <u>loses</u> 2 electrons to form a magnesium ion (Mg^{2+}).

A chlorine atom (Cl) is in <u>Group 7</u> so it <u>gains</u> 1 electron to form a chloride ion (Cl^-).

An oxygen atom (O) is in <u>Group 6</u> so it <u>gains</u> 2 electrons to form an oxide ion (O^{2-}).

A '+' by itself means the ion has a 1+ charge. A '−' by itself means the ion has a 1− charge.

Ionic Bonding

Dot and Cross Diagrams Show How Ionic Compounds are Formed

1) <u>Dot and cross diagrams</u> show how electrons are <u>arranged</u> in an atom or ion.
2) Each electron is represented by a <u>dot</u> or a <u>cross</u>.
3) So these diagrams can show which <u>atom</u> the electrons in an <u>ion</u> originally came from.

Sodium Chloride (NaCl)

The <u>sodium</u> (Na) atom loses its outer electron. It forms an <u>Na$^+$</u> ion.
The <u>chlorine</u> (Cl) atom gains the electron.
It forms a <u>Cl$^-$</u> (<u>chloride</u>) ion.

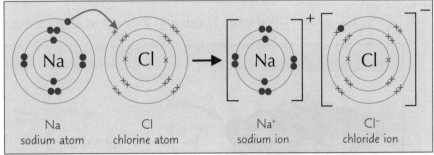

Here, the dots represent the Na electrons and the crosses represent the Cl electrons.

Magnesium Oxide (MgO)

The <u>magnesium</u> (Mg) atom loses its <u>two</u> outer electrons.
It forms an <u>Mg^{2+}</u> ion.
The <u>oxygen</u> (O) atom gains the electrons.
It forms an <u>O^{2-}</u> (<u>oxide</u>) ion.

We've only shown the outer shells of electrons in these two dot and cross diagrams. It makes it easier to see what's going on.

Magnesium Chloride (MgCl$_2$)

The <u>magnesium</u> (Mg) atom loses its <u>two</u> outer electrons. It forms an <u>Mg^{2+}</u> ion.
The two <u>chlorine</u> (Cl) atoms gain <u>one electron each</u>. They form <u>two Cl$^-$</u> (chloride) ions.

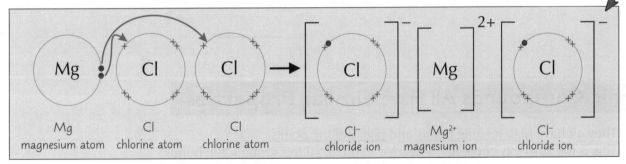

4) Dot and cross diagrams are useful for showing <u>how</u> ionic compounds are formed.
5) But they <u>don't</u> show the <u>structure</u> of the compound, the <u>size</u> of the ions or how they're <u>arranged</u>.
6) They also make it look like the electrons that are <u>crosses</u> might be <u>different</u> from the electrons that are <u>dots</u>. Really, they're all the same.

Dot and cross diagrams show the arrangement of electrons

Electrons can't just disappear, so there should always be the <u>same number</u> on each side of the dot and cross diagram. If you're asked to draw one in the exam, remember to <u>count and check</u>.

Ionic Compounds

Ionic compounds are just compounds that <u>only</u> contain <u>ionic bonds</u>. One of the main ionic compounds you need to know about is <u>sodium chloride</u>. And that's just <u>salt</u>. Nothing scary about that.

Ionic Compounds Have A **Giant Ionic Lattice** Structure

1) In ionic compounds, the ions are arranged in a <u>pattern</u>. This is called a <u>giant ionic lattice</u>.

2) There are strong <u>electrostatic forces of attraction</u> between <u>oppositely charged</u> ions.

3) These forces are called <u>ionic bonds</u> and they act in <u>all directions</u>.

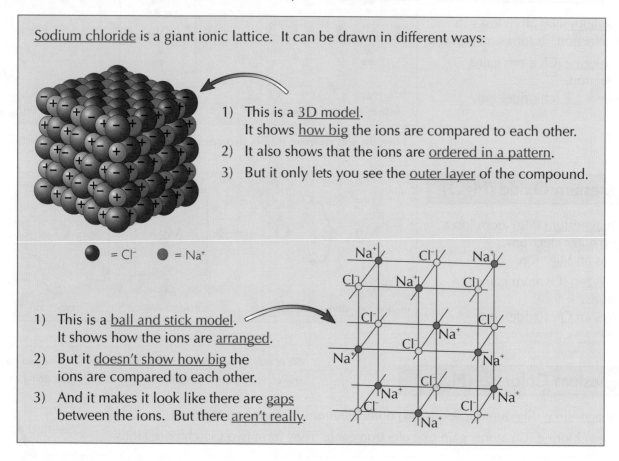

Sodium chloride is a giant ionic lattice. It can be drawn in different ways:

1) This is a <u>3D model</u>.
   It shows <u>how big</u> the ions are compared to each other.

2) It also shows that the ions are <u>ordered in a pattern</u>.

3) But it only lets you see the <u>outer layer</u> of the compound.

● = Cl⁻   ● = Na⁺

1) This is a <u>ball and stick model</u>.
   It shows how the ions are <u>arranged</u>.

2) But it <u>doesn't show how big</u> the ions are compared to each other.

3) And it makes it look like there are <u>gaps</u> between the ions. But there <u>aren't really</u>.

Ionic Compounds All Have **Similar Properties**

1) They all have <u>high melting points</u> and <u>high boiling points</u>.
   This is because lots of <u>energy</u> is needed to break all the <u>strong ionic bonds</u>.

2) When they're <u>solid</u>, the ions are held in place, so the solid compounds <u>can't conduct</u> electricity.

3) When ionic compounds <u>melt</u>, the ions are <u>free to move</u> and they <u>can conduct</u> electricity.

4) Some ionic compounds <u>dissolve</u> in water.
   The ions can <u>move</u> in the solution, so they <u>can conduct</u> electricity.

Ionic Compounds

You might need to work out the <u>empirical formula</u> of an <u>ionic compound</u> from a <u>diagram</u> — here's how.

Use **Charges** to Find the **Empirical Formula** of an Ionic Compound

1) For a <u>dot and cross</u> diagram, just <u>count up</u> and write down how <u>many</u> ions there are of <u>each element</u>.
2) For a 3D diagram, <u>use</u> the diagram to work out <u>what ions</u> are in the compound.
3) Then <u>balance</u> the charges of the ions so that the overall charge on the compound is zero.

EXAMPLE: **What's the empirical formula of the ionic compound shown below?**

The empirical formula shows the smallest ratio of particles.

◯ = Potassium ion
⬤ = Oxide ion

1) Look at the diagram to work out what ions are in the compound. — The compound contains potassium and oxide ions.

2) Work out what <u>charges</u> the ions will form. — Potassium is in Group 1 so forms 1+ ions. Oxygen is in Group 6 so forms 2− ions.

3) <u>Balance</u> the charges so the charge of the empirical formula is <u>zero</u>. — A potassium ion has a 1+ charge, so two of them are needed to balance the 2− charge of an oxide ion. The empirical formula is K_2O.

EXAMPLE: **What's the empirical formula of the ionic compound shown below?**

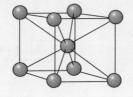

◯ = Chloride ion
⬤ = Caesium ion

1) Look at the diagram to work out what ions are in the compound. — The compound contains caesium ions and chloride ions.

2) Work out what <u>charges</u> the ions will form. — Caesium is in Group 1 so forms 1+ ions. Chlorine is in Group 7 so forms 1− ions.

3) <u>Balance</u> the charges so the charge of the empirical formula is <u>zero</u>. — A caesium ion has a 1+ charge, so you only need one to balance out the 1− charge of the chloride ion. The empirical formula is CsCl.

Ionic compounds have regular lattice structures

As long as you can find the <u>charge</u> of the ions in an ionic compound, you can work out the <u>empirical formula</u>. Try practising with different ionic compounds.

Warm-Up & Exam Questions

Congratulations, you got to the end of the pages on ions. Now test yourself with these questions...

Warm-Up Questions

1) What is an ion?
2) What is the charge on a ion formed from a Group 7 element?
3) Sodium chloride has a giant ionic structure. Does it have a high or a low boiling point?
4) True or false? Ionic compounds conduct electricity when dissolved in water.
5) What is the empirical formula of the compound containing Al^{3+} and OH^- ions only?
   A. $Al_3(OH)$ B. $Al(OH)_4$ C. $Al(OH)_3$ D. $Al(OH)_2$

Exam Questions

1   When lithium reacts with oxygen it forms the ionic compound Li_2O.

1.1   Complete **Figure 1** to show the electron arrangements and the charges on the ions when Li_2O is formed.

Figure 1

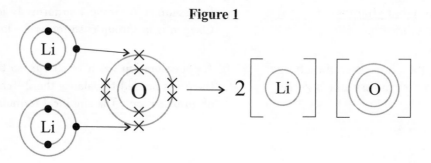

[2 marks]

1.2   What is the formula of the compound lithium forms with chlorine?
Tick **one** box.

☐ $LiCl_2$ ☐ $LiCl$ ☐ Li_2Cl ☐ $LiCl_3$

[1 mark]

2   Sodium and chlorine react to form sodium chloride, an ionic compound.

2.1   Explain how you can use the charges on the sodium and chloride ions to
determine the empirical formula of sodium chloride.

[2 marks]

2.2   Explain why sodium chloride has a high melting point.

[2 marks]

2.3   Explain why solid sodium chloride does not conduct electricity, but molten sodium chloride does.

[2 marks]

2.4   Give **one** other way, besides melting, of making sodium chloride conduct electricity.

[1 mark]

Covalent Bonding

Some elements form <u>covalent</u> bonds — they <u>share</u> electrons with each other in order to have full outer shells.

Covalent Bonds — **Sharing** Electrons

1) When <u>non-metal</u> atoms bond together, they <u>share</u> pairs of electrons to make <u>covalent bonds</u>.
2) Covalent bonds are <u>electrostatic forces</u> and are very <u>strong</u>.
3) Atoms only share electrons in their <u>outer shells</u>.
4) Atoms get one <u>extra</u> shared electron for each single <u>covalent bond</u> that they form.
5) Each atom usually makes <u>enough</u> covalent bonds to <u>fill up</u> its outer shell. This makes them very <u>stable</u>.

There are **Different Ways** of **Drawing** Covalent Bonds

Nitrogen has five outer electrons. To form <u>ammonia</u> (NH_3) it forms <u>three covalent bonds</u> to get the extra 3 electrons it needs for a <u>full outer shell</u>. Here are different ways the bonding can be <u>shown</u>:

Dot and Cross Diagrams

1) Electrons shown in the <u>overlap</u> between two atoms are <u>shared electrons</u>.
2) Dot and cross diagrams show <u>which atoms</u> the electrons in a covalent bond come from.
3) But they <u>don't</u> show how the atoms are <u>arranged</u>, or how <u>big</u> the atoms are compared to each other.

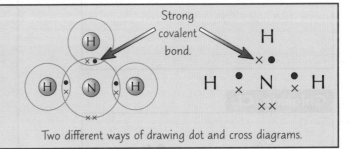

Two different ways of drawing dot and cross diagrams.

Displayed Formulas

1) <u>Displayed formulas</u> show the covalent bonds as single lines between atoms.
2) If it's a <u>single</u> covalent bond, there'll be <u>one</u> line. If it's a <u>double</u> covalent bond, there'll be <u>two</u> lines.
3) They're good for showing <u>how</u> atoms are connected in <u>large</u> molecules.
4) But they <u>don't</u> show the <u>3D structure</u> of the molecule. They also don't show <u>which atoms</u> the electrons in the covalent bond have come from.

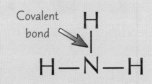

3D Models

1) 3D models show the <u>atoms</u>, the <u>covalent bonds</u> and how they're <u>arranged</u>.
2) But 3D models can be <u>confusing</u> for large molecules.
3) And they don't show <u>where</u> the electrons in the bonds have <u>come from</u>.

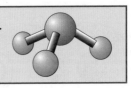

You can find the <u>molecular formula</u> of a simple molecular compound from these diagrams by <u>counting up</u> how many atoms of each element there are.

A molecular formula shows you how many atoms of each element are in a molecule.

 **Find the molecular formula of ethane from the diagram of ethane.**

In the diagram, there are two carbon atoms and six hydrogen atoms. So the molecular formula is C_2H_6.

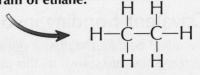

Covalent Bonding

It's always handy to have an assortment of <u>examples</u> up your sleeve when you go into a chemistry exam. You've already seen ammonia, so use this page to familiarise yourself with a <u>few more</u> important molecules.

Learn These Examples of Simple Molecular Substances

1) <u>Simple molecular substances</u> are made up of molecules that contain a <u>few atoms</u> joined together by <u>covalent bonds</u>.
2) Here are some <u>common examples</u> that you should know...

Make sure you can also draw the dot and cross diagram of ammonia, NH_3, which is on the previous page.

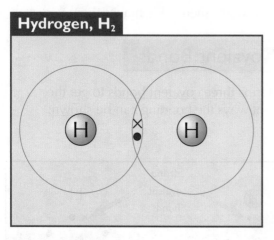

Hydrogen, H_2

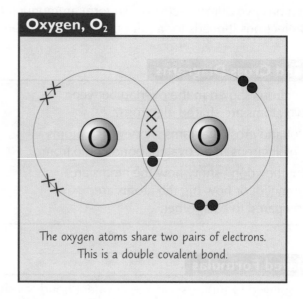

Oxygen, O_2

The oxygen atoms share two pairs of electrons. This is a double covalent bond.

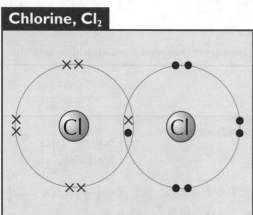

Chlorine, Cl_2

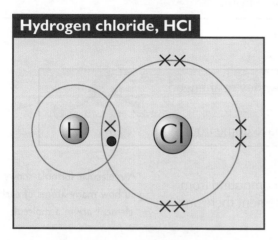

Hydrogen chloride, HCl

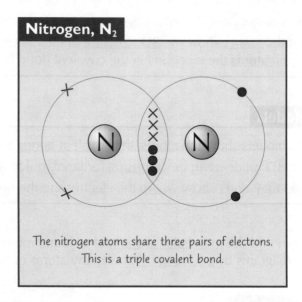

Nitrogen, N_2

The nitrogen atoms share three pairs of electrons. This is a triple covalent bond.

Covalent bonding involves sharing electrons

You might be asked to draw a <u>dot and cross diagram</u> for a simple molecule in the exam. The ones you need to know are shown on this page and the next page (oh, and don't forget to learn ammonia too).

Covalent Bonding

Just in case you can't get enough of <u>simple molecular substances</u>, here's another <u>whole page</u> on them...

Some More Examples of **Simple Molecular** Substances

Methane, CH₄

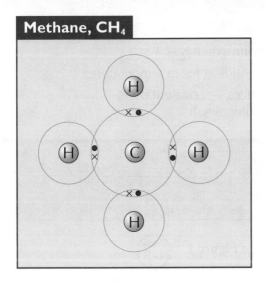

Water, H₂O

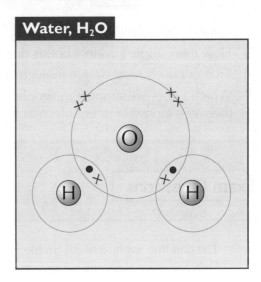

Properties of **Simple Molecular** Substances

1) Substances containing <u>covalent bonds</u> usually have <u>simple molecular structures</u>, like the examples above.

2) The atoms <u>within</u> the molecules are held together by <u>very strong covalent bonds</u>.

3) But the forces of attraction <u>between</u> these molecules are <u>very weak</u>.

Weak intermolecular forces

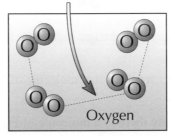

Oxygen

There's more about melting and boiling on page 63.

4) To melt or boil a simple molecular compound, you only need to break the <u>weak intermolecular forces</u> and <u>not</u> the covalent bonds.

5) So the melting and boiling points are <u>very low</u>, because it's <u>easy</u> to <u>break</u> the intermolecular forces.

6) Most molecular substances are <u>gases or liquids</u> at room temperature.

7) As molecules get <u>bigger</u>, the intermolecular forces get <u>stronger</u>.
More energy is needed to <u>break</u> the stronger forces, so the melting and boiling points <u>increase</u>.

8) Molecular compounds <u>don't conduct electricity</u> because they <u>aren't charged</u>.

Simple molecular substances are easy to melt

Remember, it's the weak forces <u>between molecules</u> that are broken when a simple molecular substance melts — <u>not</u> the strong covalent bonds between the atoms in the molecules. It's easy to get the two mixed up when you're under pressure in an exam, so get your head around it now before moving on.

Warm-Up & Exam Questions

The questions on this page are all about covalent bonding. Go through them and if you have any problems, make sure you look back at the relevant pages again until you've got to grips with it all.

Warm-Up Questions

1) What is a covalent bond?
2) How many triple covalent bonds does a molecule of nitrogen have?
3) True or false? Most simple molecular substances are solids at room temperature.
4) Which forces are stronger in simple molecular substances — covalent bonds (between atoms) or intermolecular forces (between molecules)?

Exam Questions

1 The bonding in phosphorus trichloride (PCl_3) is shown in **Figure 1**. Only the outer electrons are shown.

Figure 1

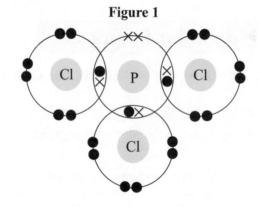

1.1 How many electrons are there in the outer shell of each atom in PCl_3?

[1 mark]

1.2 How many shared pairs of electrons are there in a molecule of PCl_3?

[1 mark]

1.3 How many double covalent bonds are there in a molecule of PCl_3?

☐ 0   ☐ 1   ☐ 2   ☐ 3

[1 mark]

2 Draw a dot and cross diagram for a molecule of hydrogen (H_2).

[1 mark]

3 Hydrogen chloride is a simple molecular substance. (Grade 4-5)

3.1 How many single covalent bonds are there in a molecule of hydrogen chloride?

[1 mark]

3.2 Explain why hydrogen chloride has a low boiling point.

[1 mark]

3.3 Explain why hydrogen chloride gas has poor electrical conductivity.

[1 mark]

Polymers

Simple molecular substances aren't the only covalent compounds you need to know about — <u>polymers</u> are also made up of <u>covalent bonds</u>. Their properties are a bit different to simple molecular compounds, though.

Polymers Have **Very Large** Molecules

1) In a polymer, lots of <u>small units</u> are joined together to form a <u>long molecule</u>.

2) All the atoms in a polymer are joined by strong <u>covalent bonds</u>.

Instead of drawing out a whole polymer, you can draw a small part of it, called the <u>repeating unit</u>. The polymer is made up of this unit <u>repeated</u> over and over again.

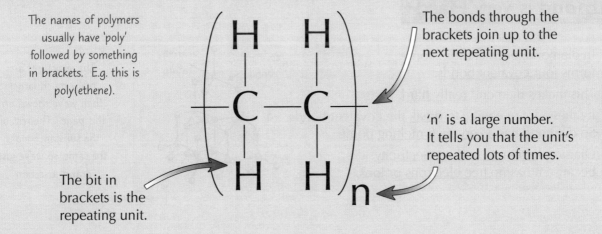

The names of polymers usually have 'poly' followed by something in brackets. E.g. this is poly(ethene).

The bonds through the brackets join up to the next repeating unit.

'n' is a large number. It tells you that the unit's repeated lots of times.

The bit in brackets is the repeating unit.

To find the <u>molecular formula</u> of a polymer...

* Write down the molecular formula of the <u>repeating unit</u>. Put <u>brackets</u> around it. Then put an '<u>n</u>' outside.
* So for the polymer above, the molecular formula of the polymer is $(C_2H_4)_n$.

3) The intermolecular forces between polymer molecules are <u>larger</u> than between simple covalent molecules. This means <u>more energy</u> is needed to break them. So most polymers are <u>solid</u> at room temperature.

4) The intermolecular forces are still <u>weaker</u> than ionic or covalent bonds. This means they generally have <u>lower</u> melting and boiling points than <u>ionic</u> or <u>giant covalent</u> (see next page) compounds.

Polymers contain lots of strong covalent bonds

You've probably heard of a few <u>polymers</u> before — ones like polyesters and polystyrene are used a lot in our day-to-day lives. Polymers are <u>really useful</u> materials, so you need to be able to recognise them.

Giant Covalent Structures

That's right — there's another class of <u>covalent structures</u> you need to know about. Here we go...

Giant Covalent Structures Include Diamond, Graphite and Silica

1) In <u>giant covalent</u> structures, <u>all</u> the atoms are <u>bonded</u> to <u>each other</u> by <u>strong</u> covalent bonds.

2) They have <u>very high</u> melting and boiling points.
   This is because lots of energy is needed to break the covalent bonds between the atoms.

3) They <u>don't</u> contain charged particles, so they <u>don't conduct electricity</u> (except for a few weird exceptions such as graphite, see below).

4) The examples you should know about are <u>diamond</u> and <u>graphite</u>, which are both made from <u>carbon atoms</u> only, and <u>silicon dioxide</u> (silica).

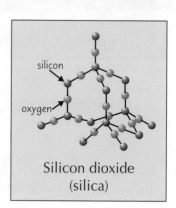

Silicon dioxide
(silica)

Diamond is Very Hard

1) In diamond, each carbon atom forms <u>four covalent bonds</u>.

2) This makes diamond <u>really hard</u>.

3) It takes a lot of energy to <u>break</u> the covalent bonds. So diamond has a <u>very high melting point</u>.

4) Diamond <u>doesn't conduct electricity</u> because it has <u>no free electrons</u> or ions.

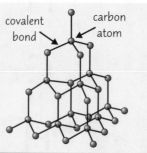

The structures are really much larger than we've shown on this page. The rest of the substance looks the same, so we've just drawn a section.

Graphite Contains Layers of Hexagons

1) Graphite contains <u>layers</u> of <u>carbon atoms</u>. The carbon atoms are arranged in <u>hexagons</u> (rings of six carbon atoms).

2) Each carbon atom forms <u>three covalent bonds</u>.

3) There <u>aren't</u> any covalent bonds <u>between</u> the layers. So the layers can move over each other. This makes graphite <u>soft</u> and <u>slippery</u>.

4) <u>Lots of energy</u> is needed to break the covalent bonds in the layers. So graphite has a <u>high melting point</u>.

5) Each carbon atom has <u>one</u> electron that's <u>free to move</u> (delocalised). So graphite <u>conducts electricity</u> and <u>thermal energy</u> (heat) — a bit like a metal does (see p.60).

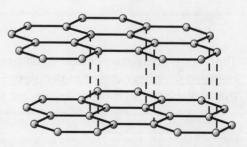

Giant covalent structures have high melting and boiling points

Unlike a simple molecular structure, you <u>do</u> have to break the <u>very strong</u> covalent bonds between atoms in order to melt or boil a <u>giant covalent structure</u>. This gives them very high melting and boiling points.

Giant Covalent Structures

Along with diamond and graphite, carbon atoms also make up graphene and fullerenes.

Graphene is One Layer of Graphite

1) Graphene is a sheet of carbon atoms joined together in hexagons. You can think of it as one layer of graphite.

2) The covalent bonds make it very strong. It's also very light.

3) It can be added to other materials to make composites. The graphene makes the materials stronger but not much heavier.

4) Graphene contains electrons that are free to move. So it conducts electricity. This means it could be used in electronics.

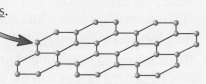

Fullerenes Form Spheres and Tubes

1) Fullerenes are molecules of carbon, shaped like closed tubes or hollow balls.

2) The carbon atoms are mainly arranged in hexagons. They can also form rings of five carbon atoms or rings of seven carbon atoms.

3) Fullerenes can be used to deliver drugs into the body. They also make great catalysts (see p.95).

4) Buckminsterfullerene (C_{60}) was the first fullerene to be found. It's shaped like a hollow sphere (ball).

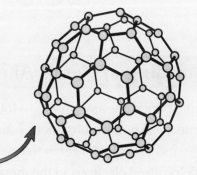

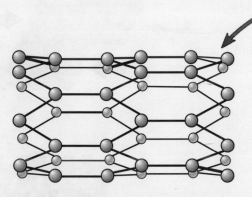

Technology that uses very small particles is called nanotechnology.

5) Fullerenes can form nanotubes — tiny carbon cylinders.

6) The ratio between the length and the diameter of nanotubes is very high (they're very long compared to their width).

7) Nanotubes have properties that make them useful in electronics. They can also be used to strengthen materials without adding much weight.

Carbon comes in many different forms

There's been quite a bit of information on the last two pages. Before you go on, make sure you can explain the properties of all these forms of carbon. Remember, just because they all contain carbon doesn't mean they're all the same — it all comes down to how the carbon atoms are arranged in the structure.

Metallic Bonding

Ever wondered what gives a metal its properties? Most of it comes down to bonding...

Metallic Bonding Involves Delocalised Electrons

1) <u>Metals</u> are <u>giant structures</u> of atoms.
   This means they contain <u>lots and lots</u> of metal atoms bonded together.

2) The electrons in the <u>outer shell</u> of the metal atoms are <u>free to move around</u> (delocalised).

3) There are strong forces of <u>electrostatic attraction</u> between
   the <u>positive metal ions</u> and the shared <u>negative electrons</u>.

4) These forces of attraction are known as <u>metallic bonds</u>.
   They <u>hold</u> the <u>atoms</u> together in a <u>regular pattern</u>.

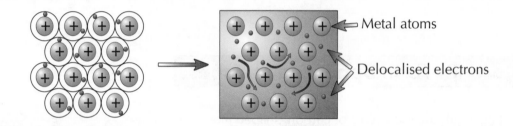

Metal atoms

Delocalised electrons

The Bonding in Metals Affects their Properties

1) Metallic bonds are very <u>strong</u>, so <u>lots of energy</u> is needed to break them.
2) This means that most substances with metallic bonds have very <u>high</u> melting and boiling points.
3) They're usually <u>solids</u> at room temperature.
4) The <u>delocalised electrons</u> in the metal are <u>free to move</u>.
5) These electrons can carry <u>electrical current</u> and <u>thermal</u> (heat) energy through the whole structure.
6) This means metals are good <u>conductors</u> of <u>electricity</u> and <u>heat</u>.
7) The layers of atoms in a metal can <u>slide</u> over each other.
8) Because of this, metals can be <u>bent</u> or <u>formed</u> into different shapes.

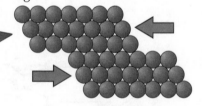

Metallic Bonding is Found in Alloys

1) <u>Pure metals</u> are often quite <u>soft</u>.
2) Most of the metals we use are <u>alloys</u>.
   An alloy is a <u>mixture</u> of <u>two or more metals</u> or a <u>metal and another element</u>.
3) Mixing another element with a pure metal causes the layers of metal atoms to <u>lose their shape</u>. This is because different elements have <u>different sized atoms</u>.
4) It becomes more <u>difficult</u> for the atoms to <u>slide</u> over each other.
5) This makes alloys <u>harder</u> and so <u>more useful</u> than pure metals.

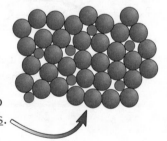

Metallic bonding is what makes metals, well... metals

The bonding between atoms is the key to understanding the <u>structure</u> and <u>properties</u> of any substance — metals included. Take a moment to check you can <u>explain</u> how they are related.

Warm-Up & Exam Questions

Lots of information to learn on the previous few pages — here are some questions to test yourself on.

Warm-Up Questions

1) True or False? The repeating units in a polymer are held together with covalent bonds.
2) At room temperature, what state are most polymers in?
3) Describe the differences in the hardness and electrical conductivity of diamond and graphite.
4) Why can most metals be bent into different shapes?

Exam Questions

1 Draw one line from each carbon structure to its description.

Carbon structure

Diamond

Graphite

Description

A structure of carbon in which each carbon atom forms four covalent bonds.

A carbon structure shaped like a closed tube or hollow ball.

A layered structure in which each carbon atom forms three covalent bonds.

[2 marks]

2 Silicon carbide has a giant covalent structure and is a solid at room temperature.

2.1 Explain, in terms of its bonding and structure, why silicon carbide has a high melting point.

[2 marks]

2.2 Give **one** other example of a substance with a giant covalent structure.

[1 mark]

3 **Figure 1** shows the arrangement of atoms in two different materials.
A is a metal and **B** is an alloy.

Figure 1

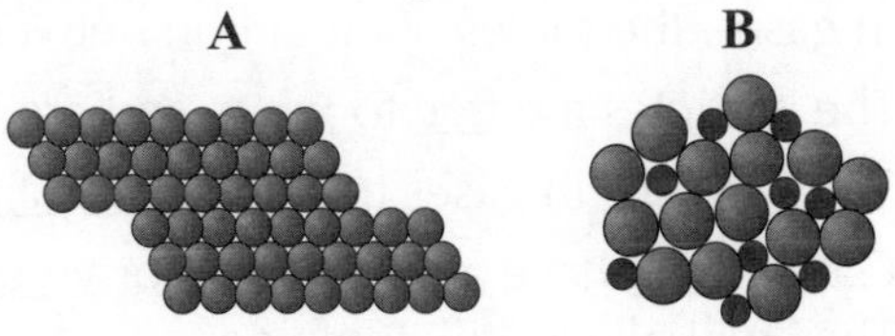

A   B

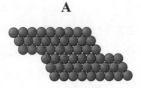

3.1 Define the term 'alloy'.

[1 mark]

3.2 Explain how delocalised electrons make metals good conductors of heat.

[2 marks]

3.3 Iron is a metal. Steel is an alloy of iron and carbon.
Explain why steel is harder than iron.

[4 marks]

States of Matter

You can explain quite a bit of stuff in <u>chemistry</u> if you can get your head around this lot.

The **Three States of Matter** — Solid, Liquid and Gas

1) Materials come in <u>three</u> different forms — <u>solid</u>, <u>liquid</u> and <u>gas</u>. These are the <u>three states of matter</u>.
2) <u>Particle theory</u> is a <u>model</u> where each particle is seen as a <u>small</u>, <u>solid sphere</u> (ball).
3) You can use <u>particle theory</u> to show what solids, liquids and gases are like.
   It can be used to explain how the particles in solids, liquids and gases <u>behave</u>.

The particles could be atoms, ions or molecules.

Solids

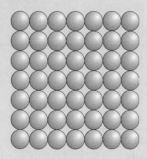

1) In solids, there are <u>strong forces</u> of attraction between particles.
2) The particles are held <u>close together</u> in <u>fixed positions</u> to form a <u>pattern</u>.
3) Solids have a <u>fixed shape</u> and <u>volume</u>.

Liquids

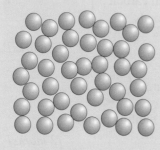

1) In liquids, there are <u>weak forces</u> of attraction between the particles.
2) They're randomly arranged and <u>free</u> to <u>move</u> past each other, but they tend to <u>stick closely together</u>.
3) Liquids have a fixed volume but <u>don't</u> keep a <u>fixed shape</u>. So they flow to fill the bottom of a container.

Gases

1) In gases, the forces of attraction between the particles are <u>very weak</u>.
2) The particles are <u>free</u> to <u>move</u> and are spaced <u>far apart</u>.
3) The particles in gases travel in <u>straight lines</u>.
4) Gases <u>don't</u> have a fixed <u>shape</u> or <u>volume</u>. They will always <u>fill</u> containers.

If you ever see something described as 'gaseous', it just means that it's a gas.

Particle theory explains solids, liquids and gases

Particle theory imagines all particles as small snooker ball-like spheres. It's not quite like that in real life, of course, but it's a good theory for understanding the <u>properties</u> and <u>behaviour</u> of the three states of matter.

States of Matter

Substances Can **Change** from **One State to Another**

Solid → Liquid → Gas

1) When a solid is <u>heated</u>, its particles gain <u>energy</u> and start to <u>move about</u>.

2) Some of the forces between the particles <u>break</u>.

3) At a <u>temperature</u> called the <u>melting point</u>, the particles have enough energy to <u>break free</u> from their positions. This is <u>MELTING</u>. The <u>solid</u> turns into a <u>liquid</u>.

4) When a liquid is <u>heated</u>, the particles get even <u>more</u> energy.

5) The forces holding the liquid together <u>weaken</u> and <u>break</u>.

6) At a temperature called the <u>boiling point</u>, the particles have <u>enough</u> energy to <u>break</u> the forces. This is <u>BOILING</u>. The <u>liquid</u> becomes a <u>gas</u>.

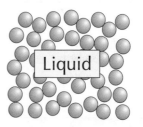

melting   freezing

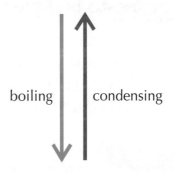

Gas → Liquid → Solid

1) As a gas <u>cools</u>, the particles have <u>less energy</u>.

2) <u>Forces form</u> between the particles.

3) At the <u>boiling point</u>, the forces between the particles are strong enough that the <u>gas</u> becomes a <u>liquid</u>. This is <u>CONDENSING</u>.

4) When a <u>liquid cools</u>, the particles have <u>less energy</u>, so move around less.

5) The <u>forces</u> between the particles become stronger.

6) At the <u>melting point</u>, the forces between the particles are so strong that they're <u>held in place</u>. The <u>liquid</u> becomes a <u>solid</u>. This is <u>FREEZING</u>.

boiling   condensing

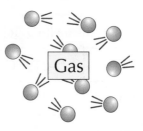

The <u>amount</u> of energy needed for a substance to <u>change state</u> depends on <u>how strong</u> the forces between particles are. The <u>stronger</u> the forces, the <u>more energy</u> is needed to break them, and so the <u>higher</u> the melting and boiling points of the substance.

States of Matter

The state a substance is in can be really important in working out how it will react. This page is all about how chemists show what the state of a substance is and how they predict what state a substance will be in.

State Symbols Tell You the State of a Substance in an Equation

1) You saw on page 21 how a chemical reaction can be shown using a symbol equation.
2) Symbol equations can include state symbols next to each substance. They're always shown in brackets, and they're normally subscripts (slightly smaller and below the rest of the letters).
3) They tell you whether each substance is a solid, a liquid, a gas or dissolved in water:

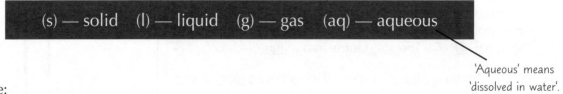

(s) — solid   (l) — liquid   (g) — gas   (aq) — aqueous

'Aqueous' means 'dissolved in water'.

For example:

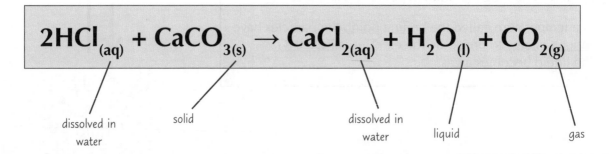

$$2HCl_{(aq)} + CaCO_{3(s)} \rightarrow CaCl_{2(aq)} + H_2O_{(l)} + CO_{2(g)}$$

dissolved in water   solid   dissolved in water   liquid   gas

You Have to be Able to Predict the State of a Substance

1) You can predict what state a substance is in at a certain temperature.
2) If the temperature's below the melting point of substance, it'll be a solid.
3) If it's above the boiling point, it'll be a gas.
4) If it's in between the two points, then it's a liquid.

The bulk properties such as the melting point of a material depend on how lots of atoms interact together. An atom on its own doesn't have these properties.

 EXAMPLE: **Which of the substances in the table is a liquid at room temperature (25 °C)?**

	melting point	boiling point
oxygen	−219 °C	−183 °C
nitrogen	−210 °C	−196 °C
bromine	−7 °C	59 °C

Oxygen and nitrogen have boiling points below 25 °C, so will both be gases at room temperature.

The answer's bromine.
It melts at −7 °C and boils at 59 °C.
So, it'll be a liquid at room temperature.

Changing between states is reversible
Make sure you can describe what happens to particles, and the forces between them, as a substance is heated and cooled. Don't forget to learn the technical terms for each state change.

Topic 2 — Bonding, Structure and Properties of Matter

Warm-Up & Exam Questions

Reckon you know all there is to know about this section? Have a go at these questions and see how you get on. If you get stuck on something — just flick back and give it another read through.

Warm-Up Questions

1) What state of matter has a fixed arrangement of particles?
2) True or false? There are only weak forces of attraction between particles in a gas.
3) Describe what happens to the bonding in a substance when it condenses.
4) How you would show that sodium ions (Na^+) are dissolved in water in a symbol equation.
   A. $Na^{+(aq)}$ B. $Na^+_{(l)}$ C. $Na^+_{(aq)}$ D. $Na^+_{(s)}$

Exam Questions

1   **Figure 1** shows a vessel in a distillery. The walls of the vessel are solid copper.

Figure 1

Complete the sentences about solids using words from the box.
Each word may be used once, more than once or not at all.

weak	move	colder	hotter	random
strong	expand	heavier	dissolve	regular

In solids, there are .... forces of attraction between particles,

which hold them in fixed positions in a .... arrangement.

The particles don't .... from their positions, so solids keep their shape.

The .... the solid becomes, the more the particles in the solid vibrate.

[4 marks]

2   **Figure 2** shows a substance changing between solid, liquid and gas states.

Figure 2

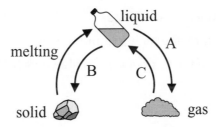

2.1   Give the letter of the arrow that represents **condensing**.

[1 mark]

2.2   Give the name of the process represented by arrow **A**.

[1 mark]

2.3   Use particle theory to explain why gases fill their containers.

[2 marks]

66

Revision Summary for Topic 2

That's Topic 2 done — time to test yourself and find out how much you actually remember.
- Try these questions and tick off each one when you get it right.
- When you've done all the questions under a heading and are completely happy with it, tick it off.

Ions and Ionic Compounds (p.47-51) ☑

1) What type of bond is formed when a metal reacts with a non-metal? ☑
2) What's the charge on the ions formed by Group 2 elements? ☑
3) Do elements from Group 1 form positive or negative ions? ☑
4) Draw dot and cross diagrams to show the formation of:
   a) sodium chloride   b) magnesium oxide   c) magnesium chloride ☑
5) Give one advantage and one disadvantage of using a ball and stick model
   to show the structure of an ionic compound. ☑
6) List three properties of ionic compounds. ☑

Covalent Substances (p.53-59) ☑

7) How do covalent bonds form? ☑
8) Draw dot and cross diagrams showing the bonding in a molecule of:
   a) ammonia (NH_3)   b) water (H_2O)   c) hydrogen chloride (HCl) ☑
9) Explain why simple molecular compounds usually have low melting points. ☑
10) What type of bonds form between the atoms in a polymer? ☑
11) Explain why graphite can conduct electricity. ☑
12) What was the first fullerene to be discovered? ☑

Metallic Bonding (p.60) ☑

13) Explain why substances with metallic structures usually have high melting points. ☑
14) Explain why substances with metallic structures can conduct electricity. ☑
15) Give one reason why alloys are more useful than metals. ☑

States of Matter (p.62-64) ☑

16) Name the three states of matter. ☑
17) What is the state symbol of an aqueous substance? ☑
18) What is the name of the temperature at which a liquid becomes a gas? ☑
19) What state will a substance be in if the temperature is above its boiling point? ☑

Relative Formula Mass

Calculating <u>relative formula mass</u> is important for lots of calculations in chemistry.
It might sound a bit hard to begin with, but it gets easier with <u>practice</u>. We'd better get cracking...

Compounds Have a **Relative Formula Mass, M_r**

To find the <u>relative formula mass</u>, M_r, of a compound, add together
the relative atomic masses of all the atoms in the <u>molecular formula</u>.

The relative atomic mass (A_r)
of an element is on the periodic
table. See page 19 for more.

 **EXAMPLES:**   **a) Find the relative formula mass of MgCl$_2$.**

In the exams, you might be given the relative
atomic masses you need in the question.

1) Look up the <u>relative atomic masses</u> of all the
elements in the compound on the periodic table.

A_r of Mg = 24 A_r of Cl = 35.5

2) <u>Add up</u> all the relative atomic masses of the atoms in the compound.

There are two chlorine atoms in MgCl$_2$, so the relative
atomic mass of chlorine needs to be multiplied by 2.

Mg + (2 × Cl) = 24 + (2 × 35.5) = 24 + 71 = 95

M_r of MgCl$_2$ = 95

b) Find the relative formula mass of Ca(OH)$_2$.

1) Look up the <u>relative atomic masses</u> of all the
elements in the compound on the periodic table.

A_r of Ca = 40 A_r of O = 16 A_r of H = 1

2) <u>Add up</u> all the relative atomic masses of the atoms in the compound.

The small number 2 after the bracket in
the formula Ca(OH)$_2$ means that there's
two of everything inside the brackets.

Ca + [(O + H) × 2] = 40 + [(16 + 1) × 2] = 40 + 34 = 74

M_r of Ca(OH)$_2$ = 74

You Can Calculate the **% Mass** of an **Element** in a **Compound**

To work out the <u>percentage mass</u> of an element in a compound, you need to use this <u>formula</u>:

$$\text{Percentage mass of an element in a compound} = \frac{A_r \times \text{number of atoms of that element}}{M_r \text{ of the compound}} \times 100$$

EXAMPLE: **Find the percentage mass of sodium (Na) in sodium bromide (NaBr).**

1) Look up the <u>relative atomic masses</u> of all the
elements in the compound on the periodic table.

A_r of Na = 23 A_r of Br = 80

2) Add up the relative atomic masses of all the atoms
in the compound to find the <u>relative formula mass</u>.

M_r of NaBr = 23 + 80 = 103

3) Use the formula to calculate the percentage mass.

$$\text{Percentage mass of sodium} = \frac{A_r \times \text{number of atoms of that element}}{M_r \text{ of the compound}} \times 100$$

$$= \frac{23 \times 1}{103} \times 100 = 22\%$$

 Relative formula mass — add up all the relative atomic masses

You'll get a <u>periodic table</u> in the exams, which could be handy for these sorts of calculations
— the <u>relative atomic mass</u> of an element is the <u>bigger number</u> next to the element's symbol.

Conservation of Mass

You've probably realised by now that you can't <u>magic</u> stuff out of thin air. It can't magically <u>disappear</u>, either.

In a Chemical Reaction, **Mass Always Stays** the **Same**

1) During a chemical reaction <u>no atoms are lost</u> and <u>no atoms are made</u>.

2) This means there are the <u>same number and types of atoms</u> on each side of a reaction equation.

3) Because of this, no mass is lost or gained — we say that mass is <u>conserved</u> (stays the same) in a reaction.

> For example: $2Li + F_2 \rightarrow 2LiF$
> In this reaction, there are <u>2 lithium atoms</u> and <u>2 fluorine atoms</u> on <u>each side</u> of the equation.

4) You can see that mass stays the same if you <u>add up</u> the relative formula masses of the substances on each side of a <u>balanced symbol equation</u>.

5) The total M_r of all the reactants will be the <u>same</u> as the total M_r of the products.

If you're not sure what the big numbers and the little numbers in reaction equations mean, see pages 20-22.

EXAMPLE: Show that mass is conserved in this reaction: $2Li + F_2 \rightarrow 2LiF$.
Relative atomic masses (A_r): Li = 7, F = 19

1) Add up the relative formula masses on the <u>left-hand side</u> of the equation.

$$2 \times A_r(Li) + M_r(F_2) = (2 \times 7) + (2 \times 19)$$
$$= 14 + 38$$
$$= 52$$

2) Add up the relative formula masses on the <u>right-hand side</u> of the equation.

$$2 \times M_r(LiF) = 2 \times (7 + 19)$$
$$= 2 \times 26$$
$$= 52$$

The total M_r on the left-hand side of the equation is the same as the total M_r on the right-hand side, so mass is conserved.

You can **Calculate** the Mass of a Reactant or Product

1) You can use the idea of conservation of mass to <u>work out</u> the mass of a reactant or product in a reaction.

2) You need to know the masses of <u>all</u> the reactants and products except for <u>one</u>.

3) You can work out the <u>total mass</u> of everything on one side of the equation.

4) You can also work out the total mass of everything on the other side of the equation, <u>except</u> for the thing you don't know the mass of.

5) The mass of the thing you <u>don't</u> know is the <u>difference</u> between these two totals.

EXAMPLE: 6 g of magnesium completely reacts with 4 g of oxygen in the following reaction:
$$2Mg + O_2 \rightarrow 2MgO$$
What mass of magnesium oxide is formed?

1) Find the total mass of reactants.   4 + 6 = 10 g

2) Magnesium oxide is the only product. So the mass of products you do know is 0 g.

Mass of magnesium oxide = 10 − 0 = 10 g

Conservation of Mass

Even though mass is always (always) conserved in a reaction, sometimes you can carry out an experiment where the mass of the reaction container changes. Time to find out why...

If the Mass **Seems to Change**, There's Usually a **Gas** Involved

In some experiments, the mass of an unsealed reaction container might change during a reaction. This usually happens for one of two reasons...

1) If One of the Reactants is a **Gas**, the Mass Could **Go Up**

If the mass goes up, it's probably because one of the things that reacts is a gas that's found in air (e.g. oxygen) and all the things that are made are solids, liquids or in solution.

1) Before the reaction, the gas is floating around in the air. It's there, but it's not trapped in the reaction container. This means you can't measure its mass.

2) When the gas reacts, its atoms become part of the product, which is held inside the reaction container.

3) So the total mass of the stuff inside the reaction container goes up.

- When a metal reacts with oxygen in an unsealed container, the mass of the container goes up.
- This is because the mass of the oxygen atoms isn't measured when they're part of the gas, but it is when they're in the metal oxide.

$$metal_{(s)} + oxygen_{(g)} \rightarrow metal\ oxide_{(s)}$$

2) If One of the Products is a **Gas**, the Mass Could **Go Down**

If the mass goes down, it's probably because one of the products is a gas and all the things that react are solids, liquids or in solution.

Remember from the particle model on page 62 that a gas will spread out to fill any container it's in. So if the reaction container isn't sealed, the gas will escape into the air.

1) Before the reaction, all the reactants are held in the reaction container.

2) If the container isn't sealed, then the gas can escape from the reaction container as it's formed.

3) It's no longer trapped in the reaction container, so you can't measure its mass.

4) This means the total mass of the stuff inside the reaction container goes down.

- When a metal carbonate is heated, it can break down to form a metal oxide and carbon dioxide gas.
  - Reactions where substances are heated and break down are called thermal decomposition reactions.
- When this happens, the mass of the reaction container will go down if it isn't sealed.
- But really, the mass of the metal oxide and the carbon dioxide formed will be the same as the mass of the metal carbonate.

$$metal\ carbonate_{(s)} \rightarrow metal\ oxide_{(s)} + carbon\ dioxide_{(g)}$$

Mass is ALWAYS conserved in a reaction...

A reaction equation is like a balanced set of scales — everything has to be the same on both sides. If it seems like it's not, the chances are there's a gas involved. So check those state symbols for the little $_{(g)}$.

Concentrations of Solutions

Lots of reactions take place between substances that are dissolved in a <u>solution</u>. And sometimes it's useful to find out the <u>mass</u> of a substance that's dissolved in a <u>solution</u>. Hold onto your hats and concentrate...

Concentration is a Measure of How Crowded Things Are

1) The <u>amount</u> of a substance (e.g. the mass) in a certain <u>volume</u> of a solution is called its <u>concentration</u>.

2) The <u>more</u> substance that's dissolved in a certain volume, the <u>more concentrated</u> the solution.

Concentration can be Measured in g/dm³

1) You can find the concentration of a solution if you know the <u>mass</u> of the substance dissolved and the <u>volume</u> of the solution.

The thing that dissolves the solid is called a 'solvent'. The solid that dissolves in the solvent is called a 'solute'.

2) The units will be <u>units of mass/units of volume</u>. For example, g/dm³.

3) Here's how to calculate the concentration of a solution in <u>grams per decimetre cubed</u> (g/dm³):

in g/dm³ ——
$$\text{concentration} = \frac{\text{mass of dissolved substance}}{\text{volume of solvent}}$$
—— in g
—— in dm³

EXAMPLES:

a) **30 g of sodium chloride is dissolved in 0.2 dm³ of water.** *1 dm³ = 1000 cm³*
What's the concentration of this solution in g/dm³?

Put the numbers into the formula to calculate the concentration. $\text{concentration} = \frac{30}{0.2} = 150 \text{ g/dm}^3$

b) **15 g of salt is dissolved in 500 cm³ of water. What's the concentration of this solution in g/dm³?**

1) The units of the volume need to be dm³ so that the units of concentration are in g/dm³.
So make the units of volume <u>dm³</u> by dividing by 1000: $500 \div 1000 = 0.5 \text{ dm}^3$

2) Now you've got the mass and the volume in the right units, just stick them in the formula: $\text{concentration} = \frac{15}{0.5} = 30 \text{ g/dm}^3$

4) You can rearrange the equation above to find the <u>mass</u> of substance dissolved in a certain <u>volume</u> of solution if you know its concentration.

5) Here's a formula triangle to help with rearranging the equation:

in g/dm³ | mass | in g
conc. × volume | in dm³

6) To use the formula triangle, just <u>cover up</u> the thing you want to find with your finger and write down what's left showing.

EXAMPLE: **A solution of magnesium chloride has a concentration of 24 g/dm³. What mass of magnesium chloride is there in 0.40 dm³ of this solution?**

1) You want to find the mass. So cover up 'mass' in the formula triangle.
This leaves 'concentration × volume'. mass = conc. × volume

2) Use this equation to calculate the mass: mass = 24 × 0.40 = 9.6 g

When you measure something like the mass of a substance or the volume of a solution, there's always some uncertainty to the measurement. You can calculate this uncertainty from a range — see pages 9 and 15 for more.

That formula triangle is very useful...

Make sure you know the equation for <u>concentration</u>. And make sure you can <u>rearrange</u> it to find the mass of solute or the volume of the solution. Plenty of practice using the <u>formula triangle</u> should help.

Warm-Up & Exam Questions

There's no getting around it — there's quite a bit of maths in Topic 3. But the best way to get good at maths questions is lots of practice. So here are some questions to help you do just that...

Warm-Up Questions

1) What is meant by the relative formula mass of a compound?
2) The A_r of hydrogen (H) is 1 and the A_r of oxygen (O) is 16. Calculate the M_r of water (H_2O).
3) True or false? Conservation of mass means that no mass is lost or gained during a reaction.
4) What does it usually mean if the mass of a container increases during a reaction?
5) A student is calculating the concentration of a solution. The mass of the dissolved substance is in grams and the volume of the solvent is in dm^3. What units should the student use for the concentration?

Exam Questions

1 Which of the following is the M_r of calcium chloride ($CaCl_2$)? **Grade 1-3**
Tick **one** box.
Relative atomic masses (A_r): Cl = 35.5, Ca = 40

☐ 54 ☐ 75.5 ☐ 111 ☐ 71

[1 mark]

2 Which of the following compounds has a relative formula mass of 62? **Grade 3-4**
Tick **one** box.
Relative atomic masses (A_r): F = 19, Na = 23, Mg = 24, Cl = 35.5, K = 39, Br = 80

☐ sodium chloride, NaCl ☐ potassium bromide, KBr

☐ magnesium fluoride, MgF_2 ☐ sodium bromide, NaBr

[1 mark]

3 Zinc carbonate decomposes when it is heated. The equation for this reaction is: **Grade 3-4**

$$ZnCO_{3(s)} \rightarrow ZnO_{(s)} + CO_{2(g)}$$
zinc carbonate → zinc oxide + carbon dioxide

In one reaction, a sample of zinc carbonate completely decomposed.
The decomposition produced 48.6 kg of zinc oxide and 26.4 kg of carbon dioxide.
Calculate the mass of zinc carbonate that decomposed.

[1 mark]

4 The formula of the compound zinc cyanide is $Zn(CN)_2$. **Grade 4-5**
Calculate the relative formula mass of zinc cyanide.

[2 marks]

Exam Questions

5   A solution of calcium hydroxide, $Ca(OH)_2$, can be known as limewater. **Grade 4-5**

5.1   Calculate the relative formula mass of calcium hydroxide, $Ca(OH)_2$.
Relative atomic masses (A_r): H = 1, O = 16, Ca = 40

[1 mark]

Calcium hydroxide reacts with nitric acid. The word equation for this reaction is:

calcium hydroxide + nitric acid → calcium nitrate + water

5.2   In one experiment, 18.5 g of calcium hydroxide reacted completely with 31.5 g of nitric acid.
9 g of water was produced in the reaction. What mass of calcium nitrate was formed?

[1 mark]

6   A student carries out the following reaction in an unsealed container: **Grade 4-5**

$$2HCl_{(aq)} + MgCO_{3(s)} \rightarrow MgCl_{2(aq)} + H_2O_{(l)} + CO_{2(g)}$$

6.1   Calculate the relative formula mass of $MgCO_3$.
Relative atomic masses (A_r): C = 12, O = 16, Mg = 24

[1 mark]

6.2   How will the mass of the reaction vessel and its contents change during the reaction?
Tick **one** box.

☐ The mass will decrease   ☐ The mass will stay the same

☐ The mass will increase   ☐ It is impossible to tell from the information given

[1 mark]

7   A teacher makes up a solution of copper sulfate to use in an experiment. **Grade 4-5**
She dissolves copper sulfate powder in 1500 cm^3 of water.
The concentration of copper sulfate in the solution is 12 g/dm^3.

7.1   Convert 1500 cm^3 to dm^3.

[1 mark]

7.2   Calculate the mass of copper sulfate the teacher used.

[2 marks]

8   The compound potassium hydroxide has the formula KOH. **Grade 4-5**
Potassium hydroxide dissolves easily in water.

8.1   A scientist dissolved 40 g of potassium hydroxide in 0.25 dm^3 of water.
Calculate the concentration of the solution formed in g/dm^3.

[2 marks]

8.2   Calculate the percentage by mass of potassium in potassium hydroxide.
Give your answer to 3 significant figures.
Relative atomic masses (A_r): H = 1, O = 16, K = 39

[3 marks]

Topic 3 — Quantitative Chemistry

Revision Summary for Topic 3

That wraps up <u>Topic 3</u> — time to test yourself and find out <u>how much you really know</u>.
- Try these questions and <u>tick off each one</u> when you <u>get it right</u>.
- When you've done <u>all the questions</u> under a heading and are <u>completely happy</u> with it, tick it off.

Masses in Reactions (p.67-69) ☑

1) How do you calculate the relative formula mass, M_r, of a substance? ☑
2) What does the number 2 in the formula Mg(OH)$_2$ tell you? ☑
3) Write down the formula for the percentage mass of an element in a compound. ☑
4) Why is mass conserved during a reaction? ☑
5) How can you use a balanced reaction equation to show that mass is conserved during that reaction? ☑
6) A certain reaction has only one product.
How could you work out the mass of the product from the reacting masses of all the reactants? ☑
7) Suggest why the mass of an unsealed reaction container might decrease during a reaction. ☑

Concentrations of Solutions (p.70) ☑

8) What is concentration? ☑
9) What do the following terms mean:
   a) solvent,
   b) solute? ☑
10) How do you convert a volume in dm^3 to a volume in cm^3? ☑
11) Give the equation for working out the concentration of a solution in g/dm^3. ☑

Acids, Bases and Their Reactions

Acids and bases crop up everywhere in chemistry — so here's the lowdown on the basics of pH...

The pH Scale Goes From 0 to 14

1) The pH scale is a measure of how acidic or alkaline a solution is.
2) The lower the pH of a solution, the more acidic it is.
3) The higher the pH of a solution, the more alkaline it is.
4) A neutral substance (e.g. pure water) has pH 7.

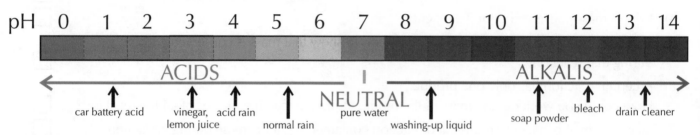

Acids and Bases Neutralise Each Other

1) When acids dissolve in water, they form solutions with a pH of less than 7.
   Acids form H^+ ions in water.
2) Bases have pHs greater than 7.
3) Alkalis are bases that dissolve in water to form solutions with a pH greater than 7.
   Alkalis form OH^- ions in water. For example, soluble metal hydroxides are alkalis.

The reaction between acids and bases is called neutralisation:

$$Acid + Base \rightarrow Salt + Water$$

Neutralisation between acids and alkalis can be shown using H^+ and OH^- ions like this:

$$H^+_{(aq)} + OH^-_{(aq)} \rightarrow H_2O_{(l)}$$

The products of neutralisation reactions have a pH of 7. This means they're neutral.

Hydrogen (H^+) ions react with hydroxide (OH^-) ions to produce water.

4) You can use a chemical called an indicator to tell when a neutralisation reaction is over.
5) An indicator is a dye that changes colour depending on whether it's above or below a certain pH.
6) The indicator is added to the acid or alkali you're neutralising. Then the other substance is gradually added. The indicator will change colour when the neutralisation reaction is over.
7) Universal indicator is an indicator that gives the colours shown on the pH scale above.
   It turns green when the pH of a solution is neutral.

There's more on indicators on page 76.

Interesting fact — your skin is slightly acidic (pH 5.5)

When you mix an acid with an alkali, hydrogen ions from the acid react with hydroxide ions from the alkali to make water. The leftover bits of the acid and alkali make a salt.

Acids, Bases and Their Reactions

There's more about <u>neutralisation reactions</u> coming up on this page...

Metal **Oxides** and Metal **Hydroxides** are **Bases**

1) <u>Metal oxides</u> and <u>metal hydroxides</u> react with <u>acids</u> in <u>neutralisation reactions</u> to form a <u>salt</u> and <u>water</u>.

2) The salt that forms depends upon the <u>acid</u> and the <u>metal ion</u> in the <u>oxide</u> or <u>hydroxide</u>.

3) HCl reacts to form <u>chlorides</u>, H_2SO_4 reacts to form <u>sulfates</u> and HNO_3 reacts to form <u>nitrates</u>.

hydrochloric acid + copper oxide → copper chloride + water
$2HCl$ + CuO → $CuCl_2$ + H_2O

sulfuric acid + potassium hydroxide → potassium sulfate + water
H_2SO_4 + $2KOH$ → K_2SO_4 + $2H_2O$

nitric acid + sodium hydroxide → sodium nitrate + water
HNO_3 + $NaOH$ → $NaNO_3$ + H_2O

Acids and Metal **Carbonates** Produce **Carbon Dioxide**

Metal carbonates are also <u>bases</u>. They react with acids to produce a salt, water and <u>carbon dioxide</u>.

sulfuric acid + calcium carbonate → calcium sulfate + water + carbon dioxide
H_2SO_4 + $CaCO_3$ → $CaSO_4$ + H_2O + CO_2

hydrochloric acid + sodium carbonate → sodium chloride + water + carbon dioxide
$2HCl$ + Na_2CO_3 → $2NaCl$ + H_2O + CO_2

Acid + Base → Salt + Water (and sometimes carbon dioxide)

There's a whole lot of <u>chemical symbols</u> and <u>equations</u> in this section, so now is a good time to make sure you're comfortable using them. Look back at pages 20-22 if you need more help.

Acids, Bases and Their Reactions

Talking about <u>acids</u> and <u>bases</u> is all well and good, but you need to know how to measure their <u>pH</u> too. You also need to know the correct method for making <u>soluble salts</u> from an acid and an insoluble base.

You Can **Measure** the pH of a Solution

1) As you saw on page 74, an <u>indicator</u> is a <u>dye</u> that <u>changes colour</u> depending on whether it's <u>above or below a certain pH</u>.

2) <u>Wide range indicators</u> are substances that <u>gradually change colour</u> as pH changes.

3) They're useful for <u>estimating</u> the pH of a solution.

4) For example, <u>Universal indicator</u> is a wide range indicator. See page 74 for a reminder of its colours.

5) A <u>pH probe</u> attached to a <u>pH meter</u> can also be used to measure pH <u>electronically</u>.

6) The probe is put in the solution and the pH is shown as a <u>number</u>. This means it's more accurate than an indicator.

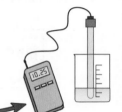

Remember, acids have a pH of less than 7.
Bases have a pH of more than 7.

You can Make **Soluble Salts** Using an **Insoluble Base**

PRACTICAL

1) If you react an <u>acid</u> with an <u>insoluble base</u> or a <u>metal</u>, you can make a <u>soluble salt</u>.

2) First, pick the <u>acid</u> that contains the same <u>negative ion</u> as the salt you want to make. For example, to make <u>copper chloride</u>, you'd choose <u>hydrochloric acid</u>.

3) Then pick an <u>insoluble base</u> with the same <u>positive ion</u> as the salt you want to make. You could use an <u>insoluble metal oxide</u>, <u>hydroxide</u>, or <u>carbonate</u>.

4) So to make <u>copper chloride</u>, you'd choose <u>copper oxide</u>, <u>copper hydroxide</u> or <u>copper carbonate</u>. Here's the equation for making copper chloride from <u>hydrochloric acid</u> and <u>copper oxide</u>:

$$CuO_{(s)} + 2HCl_{(aq)} \rightarrow CuCl_{2\,(aq)} + H_2O_{(l)}$$

5) Here's the <u>method</u> for making a <u>soluble salt</u> using an acid and an insoluble base.

---

1) Gently <u>warm</u> the dilute acid using a <u>Bunsen burner</u>, then turn off the Bunsen burner.

2) Add the <u>insoluble base</u> to the <u>acid</u> until no more reacts (you'll see the solid at the bottom of the flask).

3) <u>Filter</u> out the solid that <u>hasn't reacted</u> to get the salt solution (see p.27).

4) To get <u>pure</u>, <u>solid</u> crystals of the <u>salt</u>, you need to <u>crystallise</u> it (see p.27).

5) To do this, gently heat the solution using a <u>water bath</u> or an <u>electric heater</u>. Some of the water will <u>evaporate</u>. Stop heating the solution and leave it to <u>cool</u>.

6) <u>Crystals</u> of the salt should form, which can be <u>filtered</u> out of the solution and then <u>dried</u>.

You might get to carry these experiments out in class

Remember, you could be asked to describe how you would make a pure, dry sample of a given <u>soluble salt</u>, so make sure you understand the <u>method</u> and that you could suggest a suitable <u>acid</u> and <u>base</u> to use.

Warm-Up & Exam Questions

So you think you know everything there is to know about acids? Time to put yourself to the test.

Warm-Up Questions

1) What range of values can pH take?
2) What term is used to describe a solution with a pH of 7?
3) True or false? Universal indicator will turn blue if it is added to a substance with a pH of 7.
4) Which of the following substances is a base?
   A. $CaCO_3$ B. HCl   C. HNO_3 D. CO_2
5) Name the two substances formed when sulfuric acid reacts with copper hydroxide.

Exam Questions

1   A student had a sample of acid in a test tube. He gradually added some base to the acid.   *(Grade 3-4)*

1.1   Which negative ion is produced when a soluble base is added to an aqueous solution? Tick **one** box.

☐ H^- ☐ CO_3^{2-} ☐ O^{2-} ☐ OH^-

[1 mark]

1.2   What type of reaction took place in the student's experiment? Tick **one** box.

☐ thermal decomposition   ☐ redox   ☐ combustion   ☐ neutralisation

[1 mark]

2   All metal hydroxides are bases. They can react with acids to form a salt and water.   *(Grade 3-4)*

2.1   Sodium hydroxide is a soluble base. What name is given to bases that dissolve in water? Tick **one** box.

☐ Alkalis   ☐ Acids   ☐ Indicators   ☐ Oxides

[1 mark]

2.2   Nitric acid reacts with magnesium hydroxide to produce magnesium nitrate and water.
Complete and balance the symbol equation for this reaction. The formula of a nitrate ion is NO_3^-.

$$2HNO_3 + Mg(OH)_2 \rightarrow \text{.........................} + \text{.........................}$$

[2 marks]

PRACTICAL

3   A student is making a sample of a salt by reacting calcium carbonate with hydrochloric acid.   *(Grade 4-5)*

3.1   Name the salt formed in this reaction.

[1 mark]

The student adds solid calcium carbonate to the acid until the reaction is complete.
This is shown by a change in colour of an indicator in the solution.
The student then crystallises the solution to obtain the salt.

3.2   Suggest why the student's method will **not** produce a pure sample of the salt.

[1 mark]

3.3*   Describe a method the student could use to make a sample of the soluble salt, that does
not involve measuring the pH of the solution. Include in your answer how the student
could use filtration and crystallisation to make pure and dry crystals of the soluble salt.

[6 marks]

Metals and Their Reactivity

You can place <u>metals</u> in order of reactivity. This can be really useful for <u>predicting</u> their <u>reactions</u>.

The **Reactivity Series** — How Easily a **Metal** Reacts

1) The <u>reactivity series</u> lists metals in <u>order</u> of how <u>reactive</u> they are (their reactivity).
2) Metals react to form <u>positive ions</u>.
3) So for metals, their reactivity depends on how <u>easily</u> they lose electrons and form positive ions.
4) The <u>higher</u> up the reactivity series a metal is, the more easily it forms <u>positive ions</u>.

Make sure you learn this list.

Carbon and hydrogen are non-metals but are often included in the reactivity series.

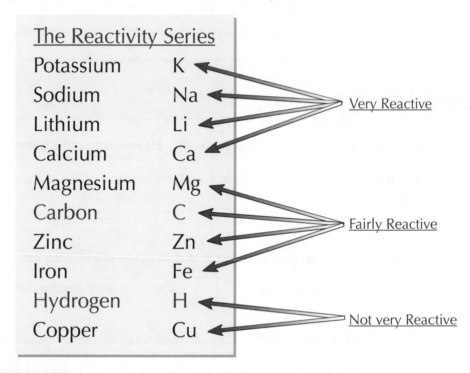

The Reactivity Series

Potassium	K	Very Reactive
Sodium	Na	
Lithium	Li	
Calcium	Ca	
Magnesium	Mg	Fairly Reactive
Carbon	C	
Zinc	Zn	
Iron	Fe	
Hydrogen	H	Not very Reactive
Copper	Cu	

Metals React With **Acids**

1) Some metals react with acids to produce a <u>salt</u> and <u>hydrogen gas</u>.

HCl reacts to form chloride salts, H_2SO_4 reacts to form sulfate salts.

$$Acid + Metal \rightarrow Salt + Hydrogen$$

hydrochloric acid + magnesium → magnesium chloride + hydrogen	$2HCl + Mg \rightarrow MgCl_2 + H_2$
sulfuric acid + zinc → zinc sulfate + hydrogen	$H_2SO_4 + Zn \rightarrow ZnSO_4 + H_2$
hydrochloric acid + iron → iron chloride + hydrogen	$2HCl + Fe \rightarrow FeCl_2 + H_2$

2) <u>Very reactive</u> metals like potassium, sodium, lithium and calcium react <u>explosively</u> with acids.
3) <u>Less reactive</u> metals such as magnesium, zinc and iron react <u>less violently</u> with acids.
4) In general, copper <u>won't</u> react with cold, dilute acids.

You need to make sure you know the reactivity series

The reactivity series is <u>useful</u> for predicting the reactions of metals, but you might not be given it in the exam. You need to <u>learn</u> it. If you're struggling, try making up a mnemonic to help you remember — or just use this one: <u>P</u>eople <u>S</u>ay <u>L</u>ong <u>C</u>alls <u>M</u>ake <u>C</u>artoon <u>Z</u>ebras <u>I</u>nto <u>H</u>appy <u>C</u>ows.

Metals and Their Reactivity

As well as reacting with acids, metals can also react with <u>water</u> and the <u>salts</u> of other metals.

Some Metals React with **Water**

1) Many metals will react with <u>water</u>.

> Metal + Water → Metal Hydroxide + Hydrogen

For example, calcium:

$$Ca_{(s)} + 2H_2O_{(l)} \rightarrow Ca(OH)_{2(aq)} + H_{2(g)}$$

2) The metals <u>potassium</u>, <u>sodium</u>, <u>lithium</u> and <u>calcium</u> will all react with water.

3) Less reactive metals like <u>zinc</u>, <u>iron</u> and <u>copper</u> won't react with water.

You Can Work Out a **Reactivity Series** from the Reactions of Metals

1) If you put metals in order from <u>most reactive</u> to <u>least reactive</u> based on their reactions with either an <u>acid</u> or <u>water</u>, the order you get is the <u>reactivity series</u> (see the previous page).

2) To compare the reactivities of metals, you could watch how quickly <u>bubbles</u> of hydrogen are formed in their reactions with water or acid. The more <u>reactive</u> the metal, the <u>faster</u> the bubbles will form.

For these experiments to be fair, the mass and surface area of the metals should be the same each time.

3) You can also measure the <u>temperature change</u> of the reaction in a set time period. The <u>more reactive</u> the metal, the greater the temperature change should be.

More Reactive Metals can **Displace** Less Reactive Metals from Salts

<u>Displacement</u> reactions involve one metal <u>kicking another one out</u> of a compound. Here's the rule:

> A <u>more reactive</u> metal will displace a <u>less reactive</u> metal from its compound.

- For example, <u>iron</u> is more reactive than <u>copper</u>. So if you add solid iron to copper sulfate solution, you get a <u>displacement reaction</u>.

- The iron kicks the copper out of copper sulfate. You end up with <u>iron sulfate solution</u> and <u>copper solid</u>.

> iron + copper sulfate → iron sulfate + copper
> $$Fe_{(s)} + CuSO_{4(aq)} \rightarrow FeSO_{4(aq)} + Cu_{(s)}$$

EXAM TIP

Metals at the top of the reactivity series are highly reactive

There are plenty of chemical equations to get your head around here. If the question doesn't ask you for a name, you can <u>save time</u> in the exam if you just write a chemical symbol instead of a full name — but always <u>check</u> that you're using the <u>right one</u>, otherwise you could lose marks.

Extracting Metals

A few metals are found in the ground in their pure forms. No such luck with the rest though — they need to be extracted from other compounds before you can use them. Here's how it works...

Metals Often Have to be Separated from their **Oxides**

1) Lots of common metals, like iron and aluminium, react with oxygen to form oxides.

2) This process is an example of oxidation.

3) These oxides are often the ores that the metals are removed (extracted) from.

4) A reaction that separates a metal from its oxide is called a reduction reaction.

An ore is a type of rock that contains metal compounds. Most metals are found in the earth as ores.

Oxidation = Gain of Oxygen

For example, magnesium is oxidised to make magnesium oxide.

$$2Mg + O_2 \rightarrow 2MgO$$

Reduction = Loss of Oxygen

For example, copper oxide is reduced to copper.

$$2CuO + C \rightarrow 2Cu + CO_2$$

Some Metals can be **Extracted** by **Reduction** with **Carbon**

1) Some metals can be extracted from their ores using a reaction with carbon.

2) In this reaction, the ore is reduced as oxygen is removed from it. Carbon gains oxygen, so it is oxidised.

3) For example:

iron(III) oxide	+	carbon	$\rightarrow$	iron	+	carbon dioxide
$2Fe_2O_3$	+	$3C$	$\rightarrow$	$4Fe$	+	$3CO_2$

Iron has lost oxygen.   Carbon has gained oxygen.

4) The reactivity series can tell you if a metal can be extracted with carbon.

- Metals above carbon in the reactivity series are extracted using electrolysis (p.82-83). This is expensive as it takes lots of energy to melt the ore and to produce the electricity.
- Electrolysis is also used to extract metals that react with carbon.
- Metals below carbon in the reactivity series can be extracted by reduction using carbon. For example, iron oxide is reduced in a blast furnace to make iron (see above).
- This is because carbon can only take the oxygen away from metals which are less reactive than carbon itself is.   *Make sure you can explain how and why different metals are extracted in different ways.*

5) Some metals are so unreactive they are found in the earth as the metal itself. For example, gold.

Carbon can't reduce things that are above it in the reactivity series

Make sure you understand the difference between reduction and oxidation and make sure that you can spot which substance has been reduced and which substance has been oxidised in a reaction.

Warm-Up & Exam Questions

Hoping to test your knowledge with some testing chemistry questions? You're in luck...

Warm-Up Questions

1) True or false? The reactivity of a metal is determined by how easily it forms a positive ion.
2) Magnesium is reacted with dilute hydrochloric acid. What is the name of the salt formed?
3) Which two substances are formed when a metal reacts with water?

Exam Questions

1   Which of the following metals would displace zinc from a solution of zinc chloride *(Grade 3-4)*
but **would not** displace calcium from a solution of calcium chloride?

☐ Magnesium   ☐ Sodium   ☐ Copper   ☐ Iron

[1 mark]

2   **Figure 1** shows part of the reactivity series of metals. *(Grade 4-5)*
Carbon and hydrogen have also been included in this reactivity series.

Figure 1

Potassium	K
Sodium	Na
Calcium	Ca
Magnesium	Mg
CARBON	C
Zinc	Zn
Iron	Fe
HYDROGEN	H
Copper	Cu

2.1   Name **one** metal from **Figure 1** that is more reactive than magnesium.

[1 mark]

2.2   Name **one** metal from **Figure 1** which would **not** displace
hydrogen from sulfuric acid.

[1 mark]

2.3   A student places a small piece of zinc into dilute acid.
The mixture produces bubbles of hydrogen gas fairly slowly.

Predict whether the reaction would be more or less violent
if iron was used instead of zinc. Explain your answer.

[2 marks]

2.4   Name **one** metal from **Figure 1** that could **not** be extracted from its ore by reduction with carbon.

[1 mark]

3   A student placed pieces of copper, zinc and an unknown metal, **X**, in zinc sulfate solution and *(Grade 4-5)*
copper sulfate solution and left them for an hour. The student's results are shown in **Table 1**.

3.1   Explain how you can tell that metal **X**
is more reactive than copper.

[1 mark]

Table 1

	zinc	copper	metal **X**
reaction with zinc sulfate	no reaction	no reaction	no reaction
reaction with copper sulfate	reaction	no reaction	reaction

3.2   Explain why there was no reaction
between copper and zinc sulfate.

[1 mark]

3.3   Suggest the name of the metal, **X**.

[1 mark]

Electrolysis

Electrolysis uses <u>electricity</u> to cause a reaction. You need to know how it works, so here we go...

Electrolysis Means 'Splitting Up with Electricity'

1) An <u>electrolyte</u> is just a <u>liquid or solution</u> that can <u>conduct electricity</u>.
   For example, an ionic compound that's either <u>dissolved</u> in water, or <u>melted</u> so it's a liquid.

2) An <u>electrode</u> is a <u>solid</u> that is put in the electrolyte and <u>conducts electricity</u>.

3) In <u>electrolysis</u>, an electric current is passed through an electrolyte.
   The ions move towards the electrodes, where they react.
   The compound then <u>breaks down</u>.

4) <u>Positive ions</u> in the electrolyte move towards the <u>cathode</u> (negative electrode).
   Here, they <u>gain</u> electrons.

5) <u>Negative ions</u> in the electrolyte move towards the <u>anode</u> (positive electrode).
   Here, they <u>lose</u> electrons.

6) The ions form the <u>uncharged element</u>. The ions are said to be <u>discharged</u> from the electrolyte.

7) A <u>flow of charge</u> is created through the <u>electrolyte</u> as the ions travel to the electrodes.

Electrolysis of Molten Ionic Solids Forms Elements

1) <u>Molten ionic compounds can</u> be electrolysed because the ions can <u>move freely</u> and conduct electricity.

2) Molten ionic liquids are always broken up into their <u>elements</u>.

3) The <u>metal</u> forms at the <u>cathode</u>. The <u>non-metal</u> is formed at the <u>anode</u>.

For example, when molten <u>lead bromide</u> is electrolysed, <u>lead</u> forms at the cathode and <u>bromine</u> forms at the anode.

See the next page for another example of how electrolysis of molten ionic compounds works.

4) The electrodes should be <u>inert</u> (unreactive) so they <u>don't react</u> with the electrolyte.

Positive ions move towards the negative electrode

It's easy to get in a muddle with electrolysis, but if you can remember that the <u>cathode</u> is the <u>negative</u> electrode and so it attracts the <u>positive metal ions</u> then you're halfway there. And the anode is just the <u>opposite</u> — it's <u>positive</u>, so it attracts the <u>negative non-metal ions</u>.

Electrolysis

You saw on page 80 how carbon can be used to <u>extract</u> some metals from their <u>ores</u>.
Now it's time to look at how <u>electrolysis</u> can also be used for extracting metals.

Metals can be **Extracted** From Their **Ores** Using **Electrolysis**

1) Aluminium is extracted from an ore that contains <u>aluminium oxide</u>, Al_2O_3.

2) Aluminium oxide has a <u>very high</u> melting point so it's mixed with a substance called <u>cryolite</u>. This <u>lowers</u> the melting point.

3) The <u>positive Al^{3+} ions</u> are attracted to the <u>negative electrode</u> where they form <u>aluminium atoms</u>.

4) The <u>negative O^{2-} ions</u> are attracted to the <u>positive electrode</u> where they react to form <u>O_2</u> molecules.

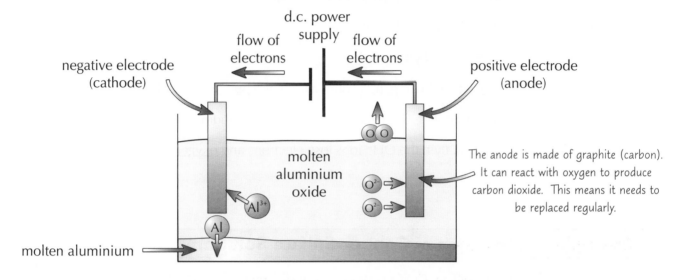

At the **Negative** Electrode

1) <u>Metals</u> form <u>positive ions</u>.
2) They're attracted to the <u>negative</u> electrode.
3) <u>Aluminium</u> is produced.

At the **Positive** Electrode

1) <u>Non-metals</u> form <u>negative ions</u>.
2) They're attracted to the <u>positive</u> electrode.
3) <u>Oxygen</u> is produced.

Overall Equation:

aluminium oxide → aluminium + oxygen
$$2Al_2O_{3(l)} \rightarrow 4Al_{(l)} + 3O_{2(g)}$$

Electrolysis is used to extract reactive metals from their ores

Extracting aluminium by electrolysis is really handy, but it does have some <u>downsides</u>. In industry, the mixture of aluminium oxide and cryolite is heated to around 960 °C. These temperatures and the electrical current used in electrolysis require large amounts of <u>energy</u>. So the whole process is <u>expensive</u>.

84

Electrolysis of Aqueous Solutions

When you electrolyse a salt that's dissolved in water, you also have to think about the ions from the <u>water</u>.

You Can **Predict** what Forms when a **Salt Solution** is **Electrolysed**

1) <u>Water</u> can break down into H+ and OH− ions.

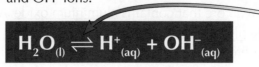

$$H_2O_{(l)} \rightleftharpoons H^+_{(aq)} + OH^-_{(aq)}$$

The $\rightleftharpoons$ symbol in this reaction shows that it's reversible. For more about reversible reactions see p.102-103.

2) So in <u>solutions</u> that contain <u>water</u>, there will be the <u>ions</u> from the ionic compound as well as <u>hydrogen ions</u> (H+) and <u>hydroxide ions</u> (OH−) from the <u>water</u>.

3) <u>H+ ions</u> and <u>metal ions</u> will move to the <u>cathode</u>.

4) If the metal's more reactive than hydrogen, <u>hydrogen gas</u> will form.

5) If the metal is <u>less reactive</u> than hydrogen, a solid layer of the <u>pure metal</u> will form.

6) If the salt contains <u>halide ions</u> (Cl−, Br−, I−), chlorine, bromine or iodine will form at the <u>anode</u>.

7) If <u>no halide ions</u> are present, then the OH− ions lose electrons and <u>oxygen</u> will form at the anode.

Example 1: Electrolysis of **Copper Sulfate Solution**

A solution of <u>copper(II) sulfate</u> (CuSO$_4$) contains <u>four different ions</u>: Cu^{2+}, SO$_4^{2-}$, H+ and OH−.

At the cathode:
- <u>Copper</u> metal is less reactive than hydrogen.
- So <u>copper metal</u> is produced.

At the anode:
- There aren't any <u>halide ions</u> present.
- So <u>oxygen</u> and <u>water</u> are produced.

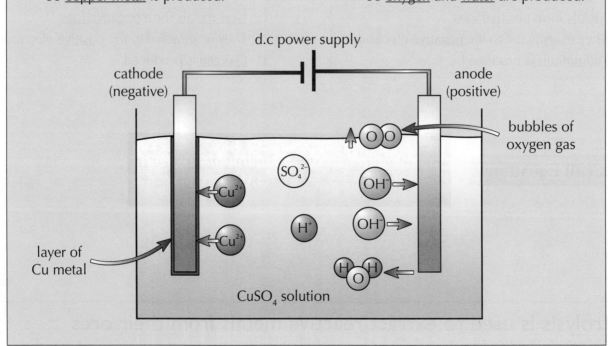

Topic 4 — Chemical Changes

Electrolysis of Aqueous Solutions

Example 2: Electrolysis of **Sodium Chloride Solution**

A solution of sodium chloride (NaCl) contains four different ions: Na^+, Cl^-, OH^- and H^+.

At the cathode:
- Sodium metal is more reactive hydrogen.
- So hydrogen gas is produced.

At the anode:
- Chloride ions are in the solution.
- So chlorine gas is produced.

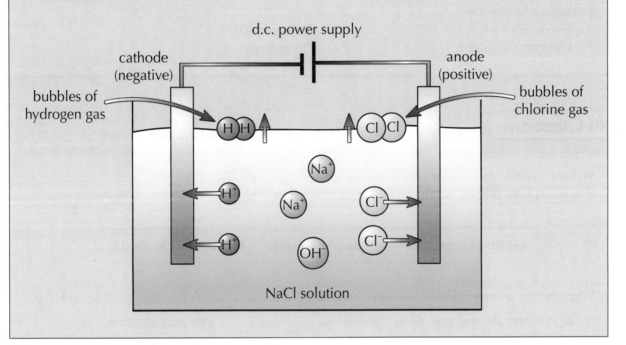

You can do **Electrolysis** in the **Lab**

1) You can set up an electrolysis experiment in the lab like the set-up on page 152.

2) This will let you collect any gases that form in the reaction.

3) Once the experiment is finished you can test the gases to work out what they are.

- Chlorine bleaches damp litmus paper, turning it white.

- Hydrogen makes a "squeaky pop" with a lighted splint.

For more on tests for gases, turn to page 121.

- Oxygen will relight a glowing splint.

Remember — all aqueous solutions contain OH⁻ and H⁺ ions

The main points to remember about the electrolysis of aqueous solutions are: 1) At the cathode, hydrogen gas is made, unless the metal ions are less reactive than hydrogen — then you get a coating of the metal. 2) At the anode, oxygen and water are made, unless halide ions are present — then the halogen is made.

Warm-Up & Exam Questions

Time to test your knowledge. Try and get through the following questions. If there's anything you're not quite sure about, have a look at the pages again until you can answer all the questions.

Warm-Up Questions

1) Are metals deposited at the anode or the cathode during electrolysis?
2) True or False? The electrolysis of molten zinc chloride produces zinc and chlorine gas.
3) What is formed at the cathode during the electrolysis of an aqueous solution of potassium hydroxide?
   A. Potassium metal   B. Hydrogen gas
   C. Oxygen and water   D. Chlorine gas

Exam Questions

1 Sodium chloride, NaCl, is an ionic compound. *(Grade 1-3)*
Use words from the box to complete the sentences below.

| negative | gaseous | sodium | aqueous | hydrogen | hydroxide |

When molten sodium chloride is electrolysed, the .... chloride ions move towards the anode and form chlorine gas. At the cathode, the .... ions gain electrons.

[2 marks]

2 **Figure 1** shows the electrolysis of molten lead bromide, PbBr$_2$. *(Grade 4-5)* **Figure 1**

2.1 Which substance is represented in **Figure 1** by the letter **W**?

☐ Br$_2$ ☐ Br$^-$
☐ Molten lead   ☐ Pb^{2+}

[1 mark]

2.2 Which substance is represented in **Figure 1** by the letter **X**?

☐ Br$_2$ ☐ Br$^-$
☐ Molten lead   ☐ Pb^{2+}

[1 mark]

2.3 Which substance is represented in **Figure 1** by the letter **Y**?

☐ Br$_2$ ☐ Br$^-$ ☐ Molten lead   ☐ Pb^{2+}

[1 mark]

2.4 Which substance is represented in **Figure 1** by the letter **Z**?

☐ Br$_2$ ☐ Br$^-$ ☐ Molten lead   ☐ Pb^{2+}

[1 mark]

Revision Summary for Topic 4

That wraps up <u>Topic 4</u> — time to put yourself to the test and find out <u>how much you really know</u>.
- Try these questions and <u>tick off each one</u> when you <u>get it right</u>.
- When you've done <u>all the questions</u> under a heading and are <u>completely happy</u> with it, tick it off.

Acids, Bases and Their Reactions (p.74-76) ☑

1) State whether the following pH values are acidic, alkaline or neutral.
   a) 9   b) 2   c) 7   d) 6 ☑
2) Give the general word equation for the reaction between an acid and a base. ☑
3) Name the products that will form when hydrochloric acid reacts with sodium carbonate. ☑
4) What do you get if you react an acid with an insoluble base? ☑

Reactions of Metals (p.78-80) ☑

5) Is copper more or less reactive than iron? ☑
6) What is the general word equation for the reaction of a metal with an acid? ☑
7) Complete the equation for the reaction of calcium with water: $Ca + ?H_2O \rightarrow ? + H_2$ ☑
8) What product forms when magnesium is oxidised by oxygen? ☑
9) Where in the reactivity series will you find metals that can be extracted by reduction with carbon? ☑

Electrolysis (p.82-85) ☑

10) What is an electrolyte? ☑
11) During electrolysis, what are the names for the positive electrode and the negative electrode? ☑
12) Aluminium can be formed by electrolysing aluminium oxide.
    Which electrode is aluminium formed at? ☑
13) A salt solution contains the ions of a metal that is more reactive than hydrogen.
    Will hydrogen gas be released if this solution is electrolysed? ☑
14) A salt solution contains halide ions. Will oxygen gas be released if this solution is electrolysed? ☑

Exothermic and Endothermic Reactions

Whenever chemical reactions occur, there are changes in <u>energy</u>. This means that when chemicals get together, things either <u>heat up</u> or <u>cool down</u>. I'll give you a heads up — this page is a good 'un.

Energy is **Moved Around** in **Chemical Reactions**

1) Chemicals <u>store</u> a certain amount of energy — and <u>different chemicals</u> store <u>different amounts</u>.

2) Sometimes, the <u>products</u> of a reaction store <u>more</u> energy than the <u>reactants</u>. This means that the products have <u>taken in</u> energy from the <u>surroundings</u> during the reaction.

3) But if the products store <u>less</u> energy, then the <u>extra</u> energy was transferred (given out) <u>to the surroundings</u> during the reaction.

4) The amount of energy transferred is the <u>difference</u> between the energy of the products and the energy of the reactants.

5) The <u>overall</u> amount of energy doesn't change. This is because energy stays the <u>same</u> (is <u>conserved</u>) in reactions — it can't be made or destroyed, only <u>moved around</u>.

6) This means the amount of energy in the <u>universe</u> always stays the <u>same</u>.

In an **Exothermic** Reaction, Energy is **Given Out**

An <u>exothermic</u> reaction is one which <u>gives out</u> energy to the <u>surroundings</u>. This is shown by a <u>rise in temperature</u> of the surroundings.

1) <u>Examples</u> of exothermic reactions include:

- • <u>Burning fuels</u> — also called <u>combustion</u>.
- • <u>Neutralisation reactions</u> (acid + alkali).
- • Many <u>oxidation reactions</u>.

Physical processes can also take in or release energy. E.g. freezing is an exothermic process, melting is endothermic.

2) Exothermic reactions have lots of everyday <u>uses</u>. For example:

- • Some <u>hand warmers</u> use an exothermic reaction to <u>release energy</u>.
- • <u>Self-heating cans</u> of hot chocolate and coffee also use <u>exothermic reactions</u> between chemicals in their bases.

In an **Endothermic** Reaction, Energy is **Taken In**

An <u>endothermic</u> reaction is one which <u>takes in</u> energy <u>from</u> the surroundings. This is shown by a <u>fall in temperature</u> of the surroundings.

1) <u>Examples</u> of endothermic reactions include:

- • The reaction between <u>citric acid</u> and <u>sodium hydrogencarbonate</u>.
- • <u>Thermal decomposition</u> (when a substance breaks down when it's heated).

2) Exothermic reactions have lots of everyday <u>uses</u>. For example:

Endothermic reactions are used in some <u>sports injury packs</u>. The chemical reaction allows the pack to become <u>instantly cooler</u> without having to put it in the <u>freezer</u>.

Measuring Energy Changes

Sometimes it's not enough to just know if a reaction is <u>endothermic</u> or <u>exothermic</u>.
You may also need to measure <u>how much</u> the <u>temperature</u> changes during a reaction.

Energy Transfer can be Measured

You can use an experiment to investigate the <u>temperature change</u> of a chemical reaction.

1) You can do this by taking the <u>temperature of the reactants</u> and <u>mixing</u> them in a <u>polystyrene cup</u>.

2) If the temperature of the solution <u>rises</u> during the reaction, record the <u>highest temperature</u> that it reaches.
If the temperature of the solution <u>falls</u> during the reaction, record the <u>lowest temperature</u> that it reaches.

3) To find the temperature change, <u>take away</u> this temperature from the temperature of the <u>reactants</u>.

4) If the temperature goes <u>up</u>, the reaction's <u>exothermic</u>.
If the temperature goes <u>down</u>, the reaction's <u>endothermic</u>.

5) The biggest <u>problem</u> with temperature measurements is the amount of energy <u>lost to the surroundings</u>.

6) You can reduce this by putting a <u>lid</u> on the polystyrene cup and putting the cup into a <u>beaker of cotton wool</u>.

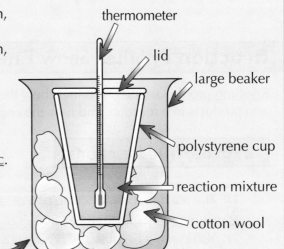

thermometer
lid
large beaker
polystyrene cup
reaction mixture
cotton wool

This method works for a number of <u>different</u> reactions. For example:

- <u>neutralisation</u> reactions.
- reactions between <u>metals</u> and <u>acids</u>.
- reactions between <u>acids</u> and <u>carbonates</u>.
- <u>displacement</u> reactions of metals.

The Temperature Change Depends on Different Variables

1) You can also use this method to investigate what effect different <u>variables</u> have on the <u>temperature change</u> — e.g. the <u>mass</u> or <u>concentration</u> of the reactants used.

2) Here's how you could test the effect of <u>acid concentration</u> on the temperature change of a <u>neutralisation</u> reaction between hydrochloric acid (HCl) and sodium hydroxide (NaOH):

1) Put 25 cm³ each of 10 g/dm³ hydrochloric acid and sodium hydroxide in <u>separate beakers</u>.
2) Place the beakers in a water bath set to 25 °C until they are both at the <u>same temperature</u> (25 °C).
3) Add the HCl followed by the NaOH to a polystyrene cup with a lid — as in the diagram above.
4) Take the temperature of the mixture <u>every 30 seconds</u>, and record the highest temperature.
5) Use your <u>results</u> to work out the <u>temperature change</u> of the reaction.
6) <u>Repeat</u> these steps using 20 g/dm³ and then 30 g/dm³ of hydrochloric acid. Then <u>compare</u> your results to see how acid concentration <u>affects</u> the temperature change of the reaction.

To get a reasonably accurate reading, insulate your reaction

It's really important the reaction mixture is well insulated in the method shown above. Without insulation, heat might escape and the temperature reading of the solution would be affected.

Reaction Profiles

Reaction profiles are handy little diagrams which show you the changes in energy during a reaction.

Activation Energy is Needed to Start a Reaction

1) The activation energy is the minimum amount of energy the reactants need to have to react when they collide with each other.

2) The greater the activation energy, the more energy needed to start the reaction. This energy has to be given, e.g. by heating the reaction mixture.

There's more on activation energy and collision theory on pages 94-95.

Reaction Profiles Show Energy Changes

Reaction profiles are diagrams that show the difference between the energies of the reactants and products in a reaction, and how the energy changes over the course of the reaction.

Reaction profiles are sometimes called energy level diagrams.

Exothermic Reactions

1) The reaction profile on the right shows an exothermic reaction.

2) You can tell because the products are at a lower energy than the reactants.

3) The difference in height between the reactants and the products shows the overall energy change in the reaction (the energy given out).

4) The rise in energy at the start shows the energy needed to start the reaction. This is the activation energy.

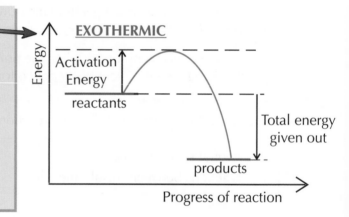

Endothermic Reactions

1) In this reaction profile, the products are at a higher energy than the reactants. So the reaction is endothermic.

2) The difference in height shows the overall energy change during the reaction (the energy taken in).

3) The rise in energy at the start is the activation energy.

You can also write the formulas for the reactants and products on the reaction profile instead of 'reactants' and 'products'.

REVISION TIP

A reaction profile shows the energy levels during a reaction

The diagrams above might seem a bit confusing at first — remember, it's the energy in the chemicals themselves, not in their surroundings, which is being shown in the diagrams. To help you remember them, why not draw them out and label them for yourself.

Warm-Up & Exam Questions

A whole bunch of reactions, an experiment, some funny diagrams — there's a lot to get your head around on the last few pages. Here are some questions so that you can check how you're getting on.

Warm-Up Questions

1) True or False? The amount of energy in the universe always stays the same.
2) Give one example of an everyday use of an exothermic reaction.
3) How will the temperature of the surroundings change during an endothermic reaction?
4) Is the reaction between citric acid and sodium hydrogencarbonate exothermic or endothermic?
5) What is shown by the difference in height between the reactants and products in the reaction profile for an exothermic reaction?

Exam Questions

1 Which of the following types of reaction is most likely to be endothermic? Tick **one** box.

☐ combustion ☐ neutralisation ☐ thermal decomposition ☐ oxidation

[1 mark]

2 A student measured the temperature change during a reaction between sodium hydroxide and hydrochloric acid using the apparatus shown in **Figure 1**.

Figure 1

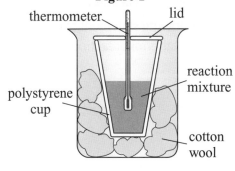

2.1 Before mixing the reagents, the student measured the temperature of each of them. Suggest why.

[1 mark]

2.2 State the purpose of the cotton wool and the lid in the experimental set-up in **Figure 1**.

[1 mark]

2.3 How could the student test the repeatability of the temperature change that they recorded during the experiment?

[2 marks]

3 The diagrams in **Figure 2** represent the energy changes in four different chemical reactions.

Figure 2

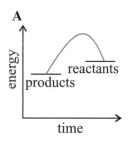
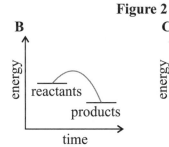
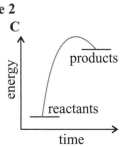
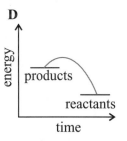

Write the letter of **one** diagram, **A**, **B**, **C** or **D**, which correctly shows an endothermic reaction.

[1 mark]

Revision Summary for Topic 5

Topic 5 — short but sweet. There's just one last page of <u>questions</u> standing between you and a <u>biscuit</u>.
- Try these questions and <u>tick off each one</u> when you <u>get it right</u>.
- When you've done <u>all the questions</u> under a heading and are <u>completely happy</u> with it, tick it off.

Exothermic and Endothermic Reactions (p.88) ☑

1) What will happen to the energy of the surroundings of a chemical reaction where the products store less energy than the reactants? ☑
2) In an exothermic reaction, is energy transferred to or from the surroundings? ☑
3) Name two different types of reaction which are exothermic. ☑
4) Define what is meant by an endothermic reaction. ☑
5) Give one example of an everyday use of an endothermic reaction. ☑

Measuring Energy Changes (p.89) ☑

6) Draw a diagram of the equipment that you would use to measure the temperature change of a reaction. ☑
7) Describe one thing that you can do to reduce the amount of energy lost to the surroundings during an experiment to measure the temperature change of a reaction. ☑
8) Give one example of a variable that the temperature change of a reaction depends on. ☑

Reaction Profiles (p.90) ☑

9) What is the activation energy of a reaction? ☑
10) Sketch a reaction profile for an exothermic reaction. ☑
11) What does the rise in energy at the start of a reaction profile represent? ☑
12) Is the following statement true or false?
In an endothermic reaction, the products of the reaction have more energy than the reactants. ☑

Rates of Reaction

Rates of reaction are pretty <u>important</u>. In <u>industry</u>, the <u>faster</u> you make <u>chemicals</u>, the <u>faster</u> you make <u>money</u>.

The **Speed** of a **Reaction** is Called its **Rate**

1) The <u>rate</u> of a chemical reaction is how <u>fast</u> the <u>reactants</u> are changed into <u>products</u>.

2) Some reactions are very <u>slow</u>, for example, rusting. Others, like burning, are <u>fast</u>.

3) <u>Graphs</u> can show you how the rate (speed) of a reaction changes.

4) The <u>steeper</u> the line on the graph, the <u>faster</u> the rate of reaction.

5) <u>Over time</u> the line becomes <u>less steep</u> as the reactants are <u>used up</u>.

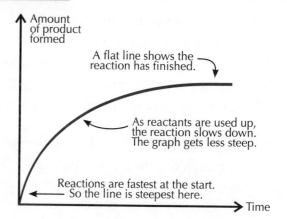

Reaction Rates Can **Change** when the Reaction **Conditions** Change

1) Faster <u>reactions</u> have <u>steeper</u> lines to begin with and become <u>flat</u> more quickly.

2) The graph below shows how the <u>speed</u> of a particular reaction changes under <u>different conditions</u>.

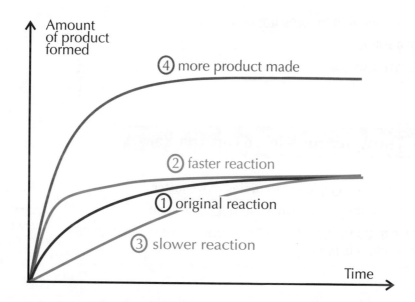

- Line 1 shows the <u>original reaction</u>.
- Line 2 shows the same reaction taking place <u>faster</u>. It starts more <u>steeply</u> than line 1. It also goes <u>flat sooner</u>.
- Line 3 shows the same reaction taking place more <u>slowly</u>. It <u>isn't</u> as <u>steep</u> at the start as line 1 and goes <u>flat later</u>.
- Lines 1, 2 and 3 all meet at the <u>same level</u>. This shows that they all produce the <u>same amount</u> of product. They just take <u>different times</u> to produce it.
- Line 4 shows <u>more product</u> is formed. This can only happen if there were <u>more reactants</u> at the start.

Factors Affecting Rates of Reaction

I'd ask you to <u>guess</u> what these two pages are about, but the <u>title</u> pretty much says it all really. Read on...

Particles Must **Collide** with **Enough Energy** in Order to **React**

1) Reaction rates can be explained by an idea called <u>collision theory</u>.
2) Collision theory says that a <u>reaction</u> will <u>only</u> take place when particles <u>collide</u> (crash into each other).
3) The particles also have to have a certain amount of <u>energy</u> when they collide, otherwise they won't <u>react</u>.
4) The <u>minimum</u> (smallest) amount of energy they need is called the <u>activation energy</u>.
5) Collision theory can explain rates of reactions in a bit more detail too...

- The more <u>often</u> the particles collide, the <u>faster</u> the reaction will happen.
- For example, if the reactant particles in a certain reaction collide with enough energy <u>twice as often</u>, the reaction will happen <u>twice as fast</u>.
- The <u>more energy</u> the particles have, the <u>faster</u> the reaction will be.
- This is because there's more chance that they'll have <u>at least</u> the <u>activation energy</u>.

How often the particles collide is sometimes called the 'collision frequency'.

The **Rate of Reaction** Depends on **Four Things**

1) <u>Temperature</u>.
2) <u>Concentration</u> of a solution (or <u>pressure</u> of a gas).
3) <u>Surface area</u> of a solid.
4) Whether a <u>catalyst</u> is used.

Increasing the **Temperature** Increases the Rate

1) When temperature <u>increases</u>, the particles move <u>faster</u>.
2) If they move faster, they collide more <u>frequently</u> (often).
3) They also have <u>more energy</u>, so <u>more collisions</u> have <u>enough energy</u> to make the reaction happen.

If particles collide twice as often with enough energy to react, the rate of reaction will be twice as fast. If they collide three times as often it'll be three times as fast.

Increasing the **Concentration** or **Pressure** Increases the Rate

1) If a solution is more <u>concentrated</u>, it has <u>more particles</u> in the <u>same volume</u>.
2) And when the <u>pressure</u> of a gas is increased, it means the <u>same number</u> of particles are now in a <u>smaller space</u>.
3) So <u>collisions</u> between the reactant particles are <u>more frequent</u>.

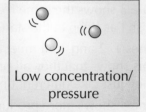

Low concentration/ pressure

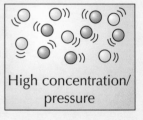

High concentration/ pressure

Factors Affecting Rates of Reaction

Increasing the **Surface Area** Increases the Rate

1) If one of the reactants is a <u>solid</u>, then breaking it up into <u>smaller pieces</u> will <u>increase</u> its <u>surface area to volume ratio</u>.

2) This means the same amount of solid has a <u>bigger surface area</u>.

3) So <u>more</u> of the solid's particles are available to particles of the other reactant. And collisions will be <u>more frequent</u>.

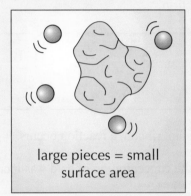

large pieces = small surface area

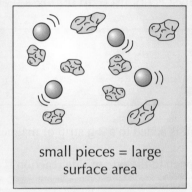

small pieces = large surface area

Using a **Catalyst** Increases the Rate

1) A catalyst is a substance that <u>speeds up</u> a reaction. <u>None</u> of it gets <u>used up</u> in the reaction.

2) This means it's <u>not</u> part of the reaction <u>equation</u>.

3) <u>Different</u> catalysts are needed for different reactions.

4) Catalysts work by providing a <u>different pathway</u> for a reaction. The new pathway has a lower <u>activation energy</u>, so less energy is needed for the reaction to happen.

5) <u>Enzymes</u> are <u>biological catalysts</u> — they catalyse reactions in <u>living things</u>.

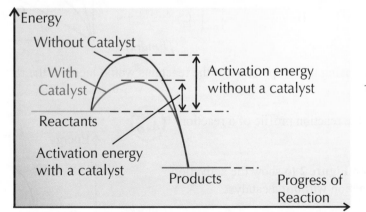

This is a reaction profile. There's more on these on p.90.

It's easier to learn stuff when you know the reasons for it

Once you've learnt everything off these two pages, the rates of reaction stuff should start making a lot more sense to you. The idea's fairly simple — the <u>more often</u> particles bump into each other, and the <u>harder they hit</u> when they do, the <u>faster</u> the reaction happens.

Warm-Up & Exam Questions

It's easy to think that you've understood something when you've just read through it. These questions should test whether you really understand the previous chunk of pages, and get you set for the next bit.

Warm-Up Questions

1) Give an example of a reaction that happens very slowly, and a reaction that is very fast.
2) According to collision theory, what must happen in order for two particles to react?
3) Explain why breaking a solid reactant into smaller pieces can affect the rate of a reaction.
4) True or False? A catalyst is not used up during a reaction.

Exam Questions

1 When hydrochloric acid is added to a 2 g strip of magnesium ribbon, a reaction occurs.   *(Grade 1-3)*

1.1 Predict what would happen to the rate of this reaction if the concentration of acid was increased.

[1 mark]

1.2 Predict what would happen to the rate of this reaction if 2 g of powdered magnesium was used instead of the strip of magnesium ribbon.

[1 mark]

2 **Figure 1** shows how the speed of a reaction changed under three different conditions.   *(Grade 4-5)*

2.1 Which line shows the reaction that produced the most product? Tick **one** box.

☐ A   ☐ B   ☐ C

[1 mark]

2.2 Which line shows the slowest reaction?
Tick **one** box.

☐ A   ☐ B   ☐ C

[1 mark]

Figure 1

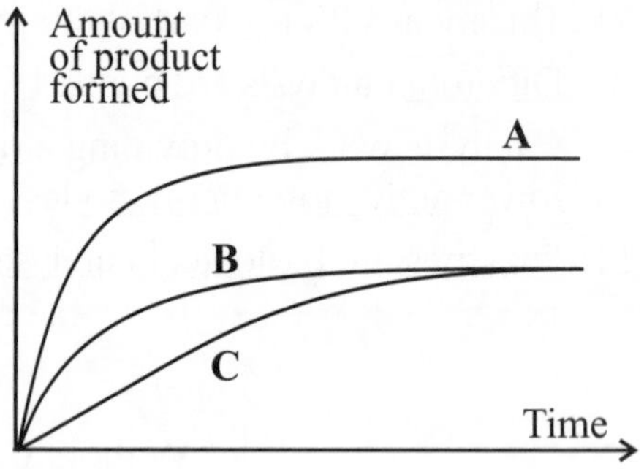

2.3 Explain why increasing the temperature of the reactants would increase the rate of the slowest reaction.

[4 marks]

3 **Figure 2** shows the reaction profile of a reaction without a catalyst.   *(Grade 4-5)*

3.1 Draw an arrow on **Figure 2** to show the activation energy of the reaction **without** a catalyst.

[1 mark]

3.2 On **Figure 2**, draw a curve to show what the reaction profile would look like **with** a catalyst.

[1 mark]

Figure 2

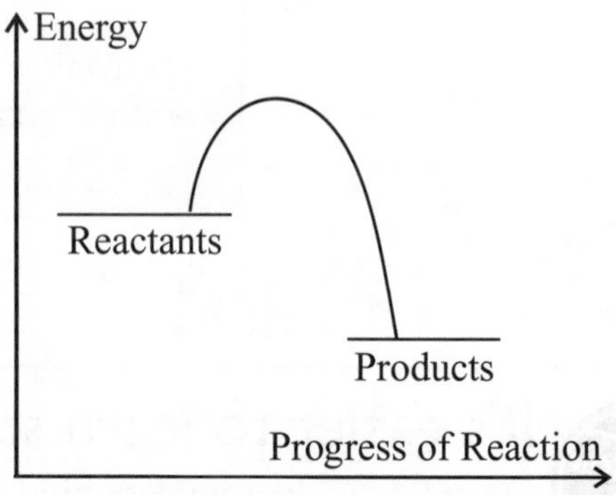

Measuring Rates of Reaction

All this talk about reaction rate is fine and dandy, but it's no good if you can't measure it. You can investigate how concentration affects the rate of a reaction by measuring the volume of gas given off.

Marble Chips and Hydrochloric Acid React to Produce a Gas

1) Measure out a set volume of dilute hydrochloric acid using a measuring cylinder.

2) Carefully pour it into a conical flask.

3) Measure out a set mass of marble chips.

4) Add the marble chips to the flask and quickly attach a delivery tube and gas syringe to the flask. You need to do this quickly before any gas escapes.

5) Start the stopwatch straight away.

6) Carbon dioxide gas will start to collect in the gas syringe. Take readings of the volume of gas at regular intervals (e.g. every 10 seconds) and write them into a table.

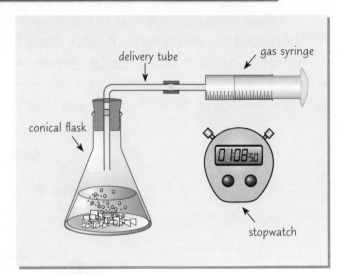

Gas syringes usually give volumes to the nearest cm³, so they're quite accurate.
Be careful though — if the reaction is too vigorous, you could blow the plunger out of the syringe.

Repeat the Experiment Using Different Concentrations of Acid

1) To investigate the effect of concentration on the rate of reaction, you'll need to repeat the experiment using different concentrations of acid. For example, you might use three different concentrations.

2) To make your experiment a fair test, you should only change the concentration of acid.

3) All the other variables (that's everything else) need to be kept the same. For example, keep the volume of acid, the mass of marble chips and the temperature the same each time.

You Then Need to Interpret Your Results

1) The more gas given off in a set amount of time, the faster the reaction.

2) You can use the results in your table to draw a graph. This makes it easier to see how concentration has affected the rate. (See pages 100 and 101 for more on drawing graphs and calculating rates.)

Measuring the volume of gas means you can find the rate

As exciting as everything on this page is, don't get carried away and forget about safety precautions — working with acids and gases can be dangerous. Always wear safety goggles, and make sure you don't let harmful gases escape into the room.

98

 **Measuring Rates of Reaction**

Measuring the volume of gas given off isn't the only way of investigating the rate of a reaction. There are two more methods you need to be familiar with.

You Can Use a **Mass Balance** to Measure **Amount** of **Gas Produced**

1) As the gas forms and escapes from the container, the <u>mass</u> of the reaction mixture <u>falls</u>.
2) The <u>quicker</u> the reading on the balance <u>drops</u>, the <u>faster</u> the reaction.
3) If you take measurements at <u>regular intervals</u>, you can plot a <u>graph</u>.
4) This is a <u>very accurate</u> method because the mass balance is very accurate.
5) But it does <u>release</u> the gas into the <u>room</u>. That's not good if the gas is <u>toxic</u> (poisonous).

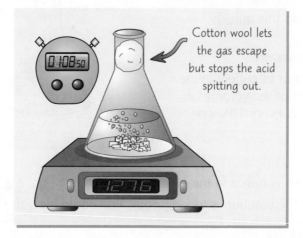

Cotton wool lets the gas escape but stops the acid spitting out.

You Can **Time** How **Long** it Takes For a **Solid Product** to Form

1) Some reactions start with a <u>transparent</u> (see-through) <u>solution</u> and produce a <u>solid product</u>.
2) The solid product (called a <u>precipitate</u>) will make the solution go <u>cloudy</u>. Another way of saying this is to say that its <u>turbidity increases</u>.
3) You can look at a <u>mark</u> through the solution and measure how long it takes for it to <u>disappear</u>. The <u>faster</u> the mark disappears, the <u>quicker</u> the reaction.
4) The results are <u>subjective</u> (there isn't just one right answer). This is because <u>people</u> might not agree over the <u>exact</u> point when the mark 'disappears'.

 ## Each of these methods has pros and cons

For example, the mass balance method is only accurate if the flask isn't <u>too hot</u>. Otherwise, the loss in mass that you see might be partly due to <u>evaporation</u> of liquid as well as the loss of gas formed during the reaction. And of course, it only works if a gas is given off during the reaction.

Measuring Rates of Reaction  PRACTICAL

Here's how to use the last method from the previous page. It's <u>less accurate</u> than using a mass balance, but you need to know how to do it in case you want to investigate a reaction that <u>doesn't produce a gas</u>.

Sodium Thiosulfate and Hydrochloric Acid Produce a Precipitate

- Sodium thiosulfate and hydrochloric acid (HCl) are both <u>clear solutions</u>. They react together to form a <u>yellow precipitate</u> of <u>sulfur</u>.
- The yellow precipitate causes the solution to turn <u>cloudy</u>.
- The <u>time taken</u> for this to happen can be measured to calculate the <u>rate of reaction</u>.

1) Start by adding a set volume of <u>dilute sodium thiosulfate</u> to a conical flask.
2) Place the flask on a piece of paper with a <u>black cross</u> drawn on it.
3) Add some <u>dilute hydrochloric acid</u> to the flask and start the stopwatch.
4) Watch the black cross <u>disappear</u> through the <u>cloudy sulfur</u> and <u>time</u> how long it takes to go.

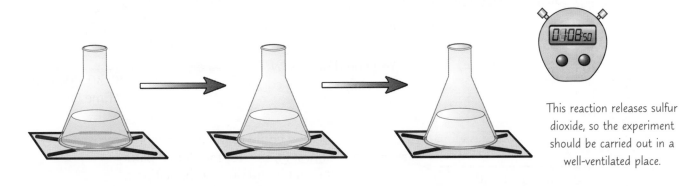

This reaction releases sulfur dioxide, so the experiment should be carried out in a well-ventilated place.

5) <u>Repeat</u> the reaction using <u>different concentrations</u> of <u>one</u> reactant, e.g. the hydrochloric acid. (Only change the concentration of <u>one reactant</u> at a time though.)
6) Make sure you <u>control</u> all the other <u>variables</u> (keep everything else the <u>same</u>). For example, the volumes of solutions, the temperature and the size of the flask all need to be kept the same.
7) You'll end up with a set of results that show <u>how long</u> it takes for the cross to disappear at <u>different concentrations</u> of acid. Like this:

Concentration of HCl (g/dm³)	20	35	50	65	80
Time taken for mark to disappear (s)	193	184	178	171	164

8) The <u>higher</u> the concentration, the <u>faster</u> the reaction, so the <u>less time</u> it takes for the mark to disappear.

Make sure you use the right method for your experiment

The method shown on this page only works if there's a <u>really obvious</u> change in the solution. If there's only a <u>small change</u> in colour, it <u>might not be possible</u> to observe and time the change.

Graphs of Reaction Rate Experiments

You might remember a bit about <u>graphs on reaction rate</u> from page 93 — well this page shows you how to <u>draw</u> and <u>interpret</u> them for <u>real experiments</u>.

You Can **Draw** a **Graph** of Your **Results**

The <u>type</u> of graph you can draw depends on what <u>experiment</u> you did.
Here's how to draw a graph to show the <u>volume of gas</u> given off during a reaction.

EXAMPLE:

Draw a graph of the results in the table.

Time (s)	0	10	20	30	40	50	60
Volume of gas (cm³)	0	9.5	15	18.5	20	20	20

1) Put <u>time</u> on the x-axis and <u>volume of gas</u> on the y-axis. (The x-axis goes along the page, the y-axis goes up it.)
2) Carefully draw a small cross to show how much gas had been produced at <u>each time interval</u>.

3) Draw a <u>line of best fit</u> through the points. You could do this by drawing a smooth <u>curve</u> of best fit.

4) Or, you could draw <u>two straight lines of best fit</u>, one for the <u>sloped</u> part of the graph and one for the <u>flat</u> part.

Tangents Help You **Compare Reaction Rates** at Different **Points**

If your graph is a <u>curve</u>, it's not always easy to see how the rate changes during a reaction. <u>Tangents</u> can help make this clearer. A tangent is a <u>straight line</u> that <u>touches</u> the curve at one point and doesn't cross it.

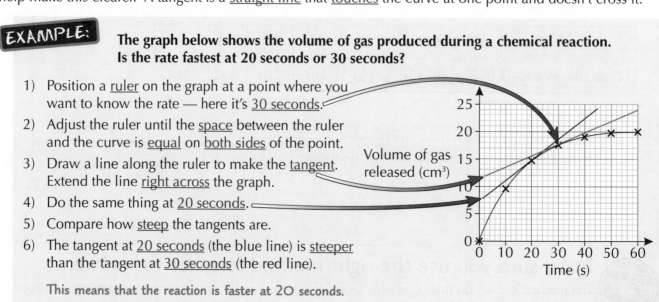

EXAMPLE:
The graph below shows the volume of gas produced during a chemical reaction. Is the rate fastest at 20 seconds or 30 seconds?

1) Position a <u>ruler</u> on the graph at a point where you want to know the rate — here it's <u>30 seconds</u>.
2) Adjust the ruler until the <u>space</u> between the ruler and the curve is <u>equal</u> on <u>both sides</u> of the point.
3) Draw a line along the ruler to make the <u>tangent</u>. Extend the line <u>right across</u> the graph.
4) Do the same thing at <u>20 seconds</u>.
5) Compare how <u>steep</u> the tangents are.
6) The tangent at <u>20 seconds</u> (the blue line) is <u>steeper</u> than the tangent at <u>30 seconds</u> (the red line).

This means that the reaction is faster at 20 seconds.

Working Out Reaction Rates

You need to be able to do some <u>calculations</u> to work out <u>reaction rates</u>.

Here's How to **Work Out** the **Rate** of a Reaction

$$\text{Mean Rate of Reaction} = \frac{\text{Amount of reactant used or amount of product formed}}{\text{Time}}$$

This equation is for <u>mean</u> rate of reaction. So it lets you work out the <u>average rate</u> over an <u>amount of time</u>.

EXAMPLE:
A reaction takes 120 seconds. 3.0 g of product are made. Find the mean rate of reaction.

Mean Rate = amount of product formed ÷ time
= 3.0 g ÷ 120 s = 0.025 g/s

Gases can be measured in cm^3, so if the product you measured was a gas the rate could be measured in cm^3/s rather than in g/s.

You Can Calculate the **Mean Reaction Rate** from a **Graph**

1) To find the <u>mean rate</u> for the <u>whole reaction</u>, start by working out when the reaction <u>finished</u>. This is when the line goes <u>flat</u>.
2) Then work out how much <u>product</u> was <u>formed</u> (or how much <u>reactant</u> was <u>used up</u>).
3) Then <u>divide this</u> by the <u>total time taken</u> for the reaction to finish.

EXAMPLE:
The graph shows the volume of gas released by a reaction, measured at regular intervals. Find the mean rate of the reaction.

1) Work out when the reaction <u>finished</u>.
   The line goes flat at 50 s.
2) Work out how much <u>product</u> was <u>formed</u>.
   20 cm^3 of gas was formed.
3) <u>Divide</u> this by the <u>time taken</u> for the reaction to finish.
   mean rate = 20 cm^3 ÷ 50 s = 0.40 cm^3/s

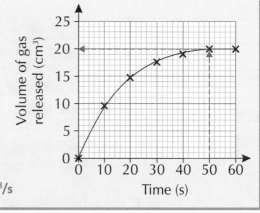

4) You can also use the graph to find the <u>mean rate</u> of reaction between <u>two points</u> in time:

EXAMPLE:
Find the mean rate of reaction between 20 s and 40 s.

1) Work out how much <u>gas</u> was produced <u>between</u> 20 s and 40 s.
   At 20 s, 15 cm^3 had been produced.
   At 40 s, 19 cm^3 had been produced.
   Volume released between 20 and 40 s was:
   19 cm^3 − 15 cm^3 = 4 cm^3
2) Work out the <u>time difference</u> between 20 s and 40 s.
   40 s − 20 s = 20 s
3) <u>Divide</u> the amount of gas produced by the time taken.
   mean rate = 4 cm^3 ÷ 20 s = 0.2 cm^3/s

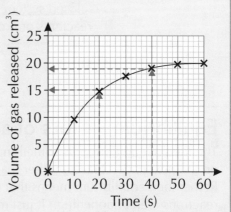

Reversible Reactions

Reversible reactions are what they sound like — <u>reactions</u> that can be <u>reversed</u>. So they can go <u>backwards</u>.

Reversible Reactions Go Both Ways

$$A + B \rightleftharpoons C + D$$

1) This equation shows a <u>reversible reaction</u>.

2) The <u>products</u> (C and D) react to form the <u>reactants</u> (A and B) again.

3) You can tell it's a reversible reaction because of the $\rightleftharpoons$ symbol.

4) The reaction of A and B is called the <u>forward reaction</u>.
   The reaction of C and D is the <u>backward reaction</u>.

Reversible Reactions Will Reach Equilibrium

1) As the <u>reactants</u> react, their concentrations <u>fall</u>.
   The <u>forward</u> reaction <u>slows down</u>.

2) As more and more <u>products</u> are made the
   <u>backward reaction</u> will <u>speed up</u>.

3) After a while the forward reaction and backward reaction
   will be going at <u>exactly the same rate</u>. The system is at <u>equilibrium</u>.

4) Equilibrium <u>doesn't</u> mean that there are the <u>same amounts</u>
   of products and reactants. It just means that the amounts
   of products and reactants <u>aren't changing</u> any more.

5) Equilibrium is only reached if the reaction takes place in a
   '<u>closed system</u>'. A <u>closed system</u> just means that <u>none</u> of the
   reactants or products can <u>escape</u> and nothing else can get <u>in</u>.

Equilibrium — lots of activity, but not to any great effect

The idea of <u>equilibrium</u> is something that you need to get to grips with, as things will get <u>more complicated</u> on the next page. Have <u>another read</u> and make sure you've got the basics sorted before moving on. Remember, equilibrium means that things are staying nice and <u>stable</u> — but that <u>doesn't</u> mean that the reactions aren't happening. It just means that the <u>amounts</u> of reactants and products <u>aren't changing</u>.

Reversible Reactions

In a reversible reaction, both the forward and the backward reactions are happening <u>at the same time</u>. Some conditions can be <u>more favourable</u> to one direction than the other, making that reaction happen faster.

Reversible Reactions Have an **Overall Direction**

1) Once a reaction is at equilibrium, there could be <u>more</u> of the <u>products</u> than reactants. When this happens, we say the equilibrium <u>favours</u> the <u>forwards direction</u>.

2) If there are <u>more reactants</u> than products then the equilibrium <u>favours</u> the <u>backwards direction</u>.

3) You can <u>change</u> the <u>direction</u> by <u>changing</u> the <u>conditions</u> (the temperature, pressure or concentration).

> - <u>Ammonium chloride</u> breaks down to form <u>ammonia</u> and <u>hydrogen chloride</u>.
> - The hydrogen chloride can then react with the ammonia to make ammonium chloride again.
> - The reaction equation is:
>
> $$\text{ammonium chloride} \underset{\text{cool}}{\overset{\text{heat}}{\rightleftharpoons}} \text{ammonia} + \text{hydrogen chloride}$$
>
> - If you <u>heat</u> this reaction, it will go in the <u>forwards</u> direction. You'll get more ammonia and hydrogen chloride.
> - If you <u>cool</u> it, it will go in the <u>backwards</u> direction. You'll get more ammonium chloride.

Reversible Reactions Can Be **Endothermic** and **Exothermic**

1) If the reaction is <u>endothermic</u> (takes in heat) in one direction, it will be <u>exothermic</u> (give out heat) in the other.

See page 88 for more on endothermic and exothermic reactions.

2) The amount of energy <u>taken in</u> by the endothermic reaction is the <u>same</u> as the amount <u>given out</u> during the exothermic reaction.

3) A good example is the <u>thermal decomposition</u> of hydrated copper sulfate:

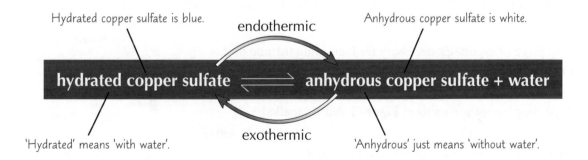

Hydrated copper sulfate is blue.   endothermic   Anhydrous copper sulfate is white.

hydrated copper sulfate $\rightleftharpoons$ **anhydrous copper sulfate + water**

'Hydrated' means 'with water'.   exothermic   'Anhydrous' just means 'without water'.

More of the products = reaction favours the forwards direction

This whole exothermic/endothermic thing is a fairly simple idea — don't be put off by the long words. Remember, "<u>exo-</u>" = <u>external</u>, "<u>-thermic</u>" = <u>heat</u>, so an exothermic reaction is one that <u>gives out</u> heat. And "<u>endo-</u>" = erm... the other one. OK, there's no easy way to remember that one. Tough.

Warm-Up & Exam Questions

Not long now 'til this section's over, but first there are some questions for you to tackle.

Warm-Up Questions

1) Name one piece of apparatus that could be used to measure the rate of a reaction that gives off a gas.
2) Reaction A forms more product than Reaction B over 30 seconds. Which reaction, A or B, has a higher rate?
3) True or false? A steep tangent on a rate graph means that the rate is slow.
4) If there are more reactants than products in a reversible reaction at equilibrium, does the equilibrium favour the forwards or backwards direction?

Exam Questions

1   In the reaction below, substances A and B react to form substances C and D.

$$2A + B \rightleftharpoons 2C + D$$

1.1   What can you deduce about this reaction from the symbol $\rightleftharpoons$?

[1 mark]

1.2   When the reaction takes place in a closed system, equilibrium is reached. Complete the sentences. Use words from the box.

equal	stay the same	forwards	rise	fall
reversible	changing	constant	backwards	

As A and B react, their concentrations will .... and the rate of the forwards reaction will

decrease. As C and D are made, the .... reaction speeds up. After a while, the amounts

of products and reactants will be .... The system is at equilibrium.

[3 marks]

PRACTICAL

2   **Figure 1** shows one method of measuring the rate of a reaction which produces a gas.

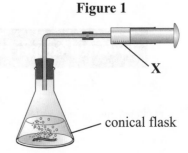

Figure 1

2.1   What piece of apparatus, necessary for measuring the rate of this reaction, is missing from **Figure 1**?

[1 mark]

2.2   Name the piece of apparatus in **Figure 1** that is labelled **X**.

[1 mark]

The rate of this reaction could also be measured using a mass balance.

2.3   Give **one** advantage of using a mass balance to measure the rate of a reaction.

[1 mark]

2.4   Give **one** possible safety concern when using a mass balance to measure the rate of this reaction.

[1 mark]

Exam Questions

3   Hydrogen peroxide is a liquid that decomposes into water and oxygen.

Samples of three catalysts with the same surface area were added to some hydrogen peroxide solution.
The same volume and concentration of hydrogen peroxide was used each time.
The volume of oxygen produced over time was measured and recorded, and is shown in **Figure 2**.

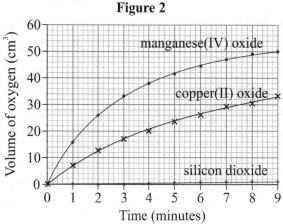

Figure 2

3.1   How much oxygen was produced in the
first 3 minutes with copper(II) oxide?

[1 mark]

3.2   Identify, with a reason, the most
effective catalyst.

[2 marks]

3.3   Describe how you could use tangents to compare
the rates of the reactions at 2 minutes.

[3 marks]

PRACTICAL

4*   A reaction between two colourless solutions, **X** and **Y**, produces a yellow precipitate.

Describe how you could use the change in colour to investigate
how the rate of this reaction changes with the concentration of Y.
Describe the method and equipment you would use, and the measurements you would make.

[4 marks]

5   **Figure 3** shows how the volume of hydrogen gas produced in a reaction varies with time.

The mean rate of a reaction is
calculated using the equation:

$$\text{Mean rate of reaction} = \frac{\text{Amount of product formed}}{\text{Time}}$$

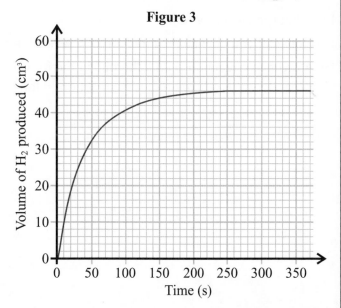

Figure 3

5.1   Use the equation to calculate the mean rate
for the whole reaction. Include appropriate
units in your answer.

[3 marks]

5.2   Use the equation to calculate the
mean rate of reaction between
40 and 150 seconds.

[3 marks]

Revision Summary for Topic 6

We'll you've almost made it — you're just one more page away from a lovely cup of tea and a biscuit...

- Try these questions and <u>tick off each one</u> when you <u>get it right</u>.
- When you've done <u>all the questions</u> under a heading and are <u>completely happy</u> with it, tick it off.

Rates of Reaction (p.93-95) ☑

1) What is meant by the rate of a chemical reaction? ☑
2) On a rate of reaction graph, what does the line getting steeper show? ☑
3) What does a flat line on a graph of amount of products against time show? ☑
4) What are the four factors that affect the rate of a chemical reaction? ☑
5) Why does increasing the temperature of a reaction mixture increase the rate of a reaction? ☑
6) If a solid is broken up into smaller pieces, what will happen to its surface area to volume ratio? ☑
7) What is a catalyst? ☑
8) How does a catalyst increase the rate of a reaction? ☑

Rates of Reaction Experiments (p.97-101) ☑

9) Describe how you could investigate the effect of increasing hydrochloric acid concentration on the rate of reaction between hydrochloric acid and magnesium. ☑
10) Explain why measuring a mass change during a reaction is an accurate method of measuring rate. ☑
11) If you're drawing a graph to show the volume of gas produced over time, what axis should time go on? ☑
12) What is a tangent? ☑
13) True or false? A tangent drawn on a rate curve at 20 seconds would have a steeper gradient than one drawn at 30 seconds. ☑
14) Give two possible units for the rate of a chemical reaction. ☑

Reversible Reactions (p.102-103) ☑

15) What symbol shows that a reaction is reversible? ☑
16) True or false? In a reaction at equilibrium, there is the same amount of products as reactants. ☑
17) What is a closed system? ☑
18) How can you change the direction of a reversible reaction? ☑
19) A reversible reaction is endothermic in the forwards direction. What does this tell you about the reaction in the backwards direction? ☑

Hydrocarbons

Organic chemistry is about compounds that contain <u>carbon</u>. <u>Hydrocarbons</u> are the simplest organic compounds. As you're about to discover, their <u>properties</u> are affected by their <u>structure</u>.

Alkanes Only Have C–C and C–H **Single** Bonds

1) <u>Hydrocarbons</u> are compounds formed from carbon and hydrogen atoms <u>only</u>.

2) <u>Alkanes</u> are the simplest type of hydrocarbon. They have the general formula:

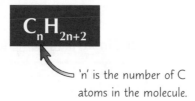

$$C_nH_{2n+2}$$

'n' is the number of C atoms in the molecule.

3) In alkanes, each carbon atom forms four <u>single covalent bonds</u>.

4) The first four alkanes are <u>methane</u>, <u>ethane</u>, <u>propane</u> and <u>butane</u>.

Methane

Formula: CH_4

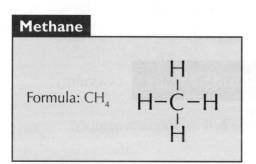

Ethane

Formula: C_2H_6

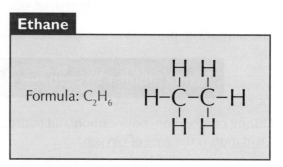

Propane

Formula: C_3H_8

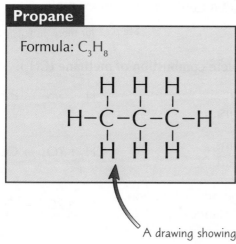

Butane

Formula: C_4H_{10}

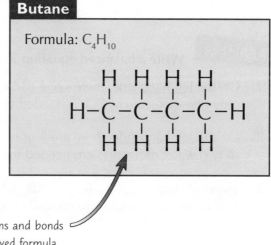

A drawing showing all the atoms and bonds in a molecule is called a displayed formula.

Hydrocarbons only contain hydrogen and carbon

To help remember the names of the <u>first four alkanes</u> just remember: <u>M</u>ice <u>E</u>at <u>P</u>eanut <u>B</u>utter. Practise drawing the structures and get to grips with their formulas using the general formula.

Hydrocarbons

Hydrocarbon **Properties Change** as the Chain Gets **Longer**

1) As the length of the carbon chain changes, the properties of the hydrocarbon change.

2) The shorter the hydrocarbon chain...

> ...the more runny a hydrocarbon is —
> that is, the less viscous (gloopy) it is.

> ...the lower its boiling point will be.

> ...the more flammable (easier to ignite) the hydrocarbon is.

Complete Combustion Occurs When There's Plenty of **Oxygen**

1) The complete combustion of a hydrocarbon in oxygen releases lots of energy.

2) This makes them useful as fuels.
The properties of the different hydrocarbons affect exactly how they're used for fuels.

3) The only waste products of complete combustion are carbon dioxide and water vapour.

> hydrocarbon + oxygen → carbon dioxide + water   (+ energy)

4) During combustion, both carbon and hydrogen from the hydrocarbon are oxidised. Oxidation is the gain of oxygen.

5) You need to be able to give a balanced symbol equation for the complete combustion of a simple hydrocarbon when you're given its molecular formula. Here's an example:

See p.22 for more on balancing equations.

EXAMPLE: **Write a balanced equation for the complete combustion of methane (CH_4).**

1) On the left hand side, there's one carbon atom, so only one molecule of CO_2 is needed to balance this.

$CH_4 + ?O_2 \rightarrow CO_2 + ?H_2O$

2) On the left hand side, there are four hydrogen atoms, so two water molecules are needed to balance them.

$CH_4 + ?O_2 \rightarrow CO_2 + 2H_2O$

3) There are four oxygen atoms on the right hand side of the equation. Two oxygen molecules are needed on the left to balance them.

$CH_4 + 2O_2 \rightarrow CO_2 + 2H_2O$

Alkanes are useful fuels as they release energy when burnt

So shorter hydrocarbons are less viscous, more volatile and easier to ignite than longer hydrocarbons.

Crude Oil

Crude oil has fuelled <u>modern life</u> — it would be a very different world if we hadn't discovered oil.

Crude Oil is Made Over a **Long Period of Time**

1) <u>Crude oil</u> is a <u>fossil fuel</u> found in <u>rocks</u>.
2) Fossil fuels are <u>natural</u> substances. They can be used as a source of <u>energy</u>.
3) Crude oil formed mainly from the remains of plankton, as well as other plants and animals. These died millions of years ago and were buried in mud.

Plankton are tiny living plants and animals which float around in oceans and other large bodies of water.

- Fossil fuels like coal, oil and gas are called <u>non-renewable fuels</u>.
- This is because they take so long to make that they're being <u>used up</u> much faster than they're being formed.
- They're <u>finite</u> resources (see p.134) — one day they'll run out.

Crude Oil has Various Important Uses in Modern Life

1) <u>Oil</u> provides the <u>fuel</u> for most modern <u>transport</u> — cars, trains, planes, the lot.

2) Diesel oil, kerosene, heavy fuel oil and LPG (liquefied petroleum gas) all come from crude oil.

3) <u>Petrochemicals</u> are compounds that come from crude oil. The <u>petrochemical industry</u> uses some of the compounds from crude oil as a <u>feedstock</u> to make <u>new compounds</u> for use in things like...

- <u>polymers</u> (e.g. plastics)
- <u>solvents</u>
- <u>lubricants</u>
- <u>detergents</u>

A feedstock is a raw material used for a chemical process.

4) All the products you get from crude oil are examples of <u>organic compounds</u>. Organic compounds are compounds containing carbon atoms.

5) Most of the organic compounds in crude oil are <u>hydrocarbons</u> (see pages 107-108). These hydrocarbons are a range of <u>different sizes</u>.

6) You can get a large <u>variety</u> of products from crude oil. This is because carbon atoms can bond together to form different groups called <u>homologous series</u>.

7) These groups contain <u>similar compounds</u> which have many <u>properties</u> in common. <u>Alkanes</u> and <u>alkenes</u> are both examples of different homologous series.

Crude oil isn't only used for fuel

Crude oil is a <u>fossil fuel</u>, but the compounds found in it are useful for manufacturing all kinds of things. Make sure you can name some <u>examples</u> of the different <u>fuels</u> that come from crude oil, and of <u>product types</u> which are made from crude oil feedstocks (e.g. detergents).

Fractional Distillation

Crude oil can be used to make loads of useful things, such as fuels. But you can't just put crude oil in your car. First, the different hydrocarbons have to be separated. That's where fractional distillation comes in.

Fractional Distillation is Used to Separate Hydrocarbon Fractions

Crude oil is a mixture of lots of different hydrocarbons, most of which are alkanes.
The different compounds in crude oil are separated by fractional distillation.

Here's how it works:

Hydrocarbons are molecules containing only hydrogen and carbon.

1) The oil is heated until most of it has evaporated (turned into gas).
   The gases enter a fractionating column (and the liquid bit is drained off).

2) In the column it's hot at the bottom and gets cooler as you go up.

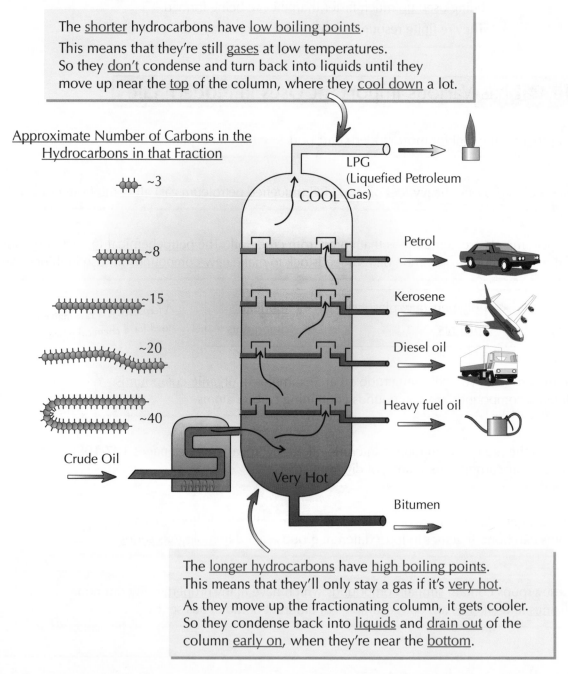

The shorter hydrocarbons have low boiling points.
This means that they're still gases at low temperatures.
So they don't condense and turn back into liquids until they
move up near the top of the column, where they cool down a lot.

Approximate Number of Carbons in the
Hydrocarbons in that Fraction

~3

~8

~15

~20

~40

Crude Oil

Very Hot

COOL

LPG
(Liquefied Petroleum Gas)

Petrol

Kerosene

Diesel oil

Heavy fuel oil

Bitumen

The longer hydrocarbons have high boiling points.
This means that they'll only stay a gas if it's very hot.

As they move up the fractionating column, it gets cooler.
So they condense back into liquids and drain out of the
column early on, when they're near the bottom.

3) You end up with the crude oil mixture separated into different fractions (parts), e.g. petrol and diesel oil.

4) Each fraction contains a mixture of hydrocarbons. All of the hydrocarbons in one fraction
   contain a similar number of carbon atoms. This means they'll have similar boiling points.

Cracking

Crude oil fractions from fractional distillation can be split into <u>smaller molecules</u>. This is called <u>cracking</u>. It's super important, otherwise we might not have enough fuel for cars and planes and things.

Cracking Means Splitting Up Long–Chain Hydrocarbons

1) There is a <u>high demand</u> for fuels with small molecules.

2) This is because <u>short-chain hydrocarbons</u> tend to be more useful than <u>long-chain hydrocarbons</u>.

3) So, lots of longer alkane molecules are <u>turned</u> into <u>smaller</u>, <u>more useful</u> ones. This is done by a process called <u>cracking</u>.

4) Some of the products of cracking are useful as <u>fuels</u>, e.g. petrol for cars.

Cracking Makes Alkanes and Alkenes

1) <u>Alkenes</u> are another type of hydrocarbon.

2) Alkenes are a lot <u>more reactive</u> than alkanes.

3) They're used as a <u>starting material</u> when making lots of other compounds and can be used to make polymers.

See p.57 for more on polymers.

Bromine Water Can Be Used To Test for Alkenes

1) When orange <u>bromine water</u> is added to an <u>alkane</u>, no reaction will happen and it'll stay <u>bright orange</u>.

2) If it's added to an <u>alkene</u>, the <u>bromine</u> reacts with the alkene to make a <u>colourless</u> compound. So the bromine water turns colourless.

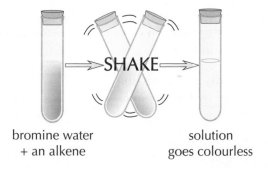

bromine water
+ an alkene

SHAKE

solution
goes colourless

Cracking produces more of the hydrocarbons we need

There's not much you can do with longer-chain hydrocarbons. But <u>shorter-chain</u> ones are useful as <u>fuels</u> and to <u>make other compounds</u> like polymers. <u>Cracking</u> means we can <u>make use</u> of all those long chain hydrocarbons that we otherwise wouldn't need, which is why it's so important to the petrochemical industry.

Cracking

There are **Different Methods** of **Cracking**

1) Cracking is a thermal decomposition reaction.
2) This means the molecules are broken down by heating them.
3) This can by done by catalytic cracking or by steam cracking.

Catalytic Cracking

1) Long-chain hydrocarbons are heated to turn them into a gas (vapour).
2) Then the vapour is passed over a hot powdered aluminium oxide catalyst.
3) The long-chain molecules split apart on the surface of the specks of catalyst.

Catalysts speed up reactions without getting used up (see p.95).

Steam Cracking

1) Long-chain hydrocarbons are heated to turn them into a gas.
2) The hydrocarbon vapour is mixed with steam.
3) They are then heated to a very high temperature which splits them into smaller molecules.

You Can Write **Equations** for Cracking Reactions

You might be asked to work out the formula of the products or reactants involved in a cracking reaction. You can do this by balancing the number of carbons and hydrogens on each side of the reaction.

Decane can be cracked to form octane and one other product. The equation for the cracking of decane, $C_{10}H_{22}$, is shown below. Complete the equation.

$$C_{10}H_{22} \rightarrow C_8H_{18} + \ldots\ldots\ldots\ldots$$

1) There needs to be the same number of carbon and hydrogen atoms on each side of the equation.

2) The number of carbon atoms in the missing product equals the number of carbons in $C_{10}H_{22}$ minus the number of carbons in C_8H_{18}.

number of C atoms = 10 − 8 = 2

3) The number of hydrogen atoms in the missing product equals the number of hydrogens in $C_{10}H_{22}$ minus the number of hydrogens in C_8H_{18}.

number of H atoms = 22 − 18 = 4

4) Put these numbers into the formula of the missing product.

$$C_{10}H_{22} \rightarrow C_8H_{18} + C_2H_4$$

Cracking always involves heating

In catalytic cracking the hydrocarbons are heated with a catalyst and in steam cracking they're heated with steam. Simple really. Which gives you plenty of time to get some more practise balancing your equations.

Warm-Up & Exam Questions

Hydrocarbons contain only hydrogen and carbon atoms.
This page contains only Warm-Up and Exam Questions. Time to get thinking.

Warm-Up Questions

1) Name the first four alkanes.
2) What type of bonds hold the atoms in alkanes together?
3) Why are alkanes often used as fuels?
4) What size hydrocarbon molecules are cracked?

Exam Questions

1 Which alkane is shown in **Figure 1**? *(Grade 3-4)*
Tick **one** box.

Figure 1

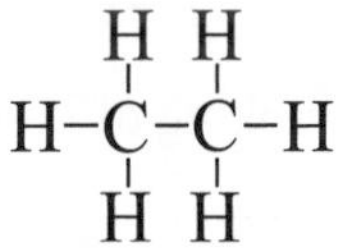

H   H
| |
H–C–C–H
| |
H   H

☐ propane   ☐ ethane   ☐ methane

[1 mark]

2 Which statement correctly describes how the properties of hydrocarbons change *(Grade 3-4)*
as the length of the carbon chain increases?
Tick **one** box.

☐ Flammability increases and viscosity increases.

☐ Flammability increases and viscosity decreases.

☐ Flammability decreases and viscosity increases.

☐ Flammability decreases and viscosity decreases.

[1 mark]

3 Alkanes are a homologous series of hydrocarbons made up of chains *(Grade 4-5)*
of carbon atoms surrounded by hydrogen atoms.

Pentane is an alkane with the formula C_5H_{12}.

3.1 Name the alkane that has one fewer carbon atoms than pentane.

[1 mark]

3.2 Give the **formula** of the alkane that has one fewer carbon atoms than pentane.

[1 mark]

3.3 Alkanes are a product made from crude oil. They are often used as fuels.
Give **two** other uses of compounds made from crude oil.

[2 marks]

4 Which of the following statements best describes what occurs during a combustion reaction? Tick **one** box.

☐ Oxygen reacts with a fuel and energy is released.

☐ A fuel takes in energy and decomposes.

☐ Carbon dioxide reacts with a fuel and energy is released.

☐ A fuel reacts with water vapour in clouds to produce acid rain.

[1 mark]

5 When nonane is cracked, heptane (an alkane) and ethene (an alkene) can be produced. **Figure 2** shows the displayed formulas of nonane, heptane and ethene.

Figure 2

H H H H H H H H H
H–C–C–C–C–C–C–C–C–C–H
H H H H H H H H H
nonane

H H H H H H H
H–C–C–C–C–C–C–C–H   heptane
H H H H H H H

H   H
  C=C
H   H   ethene

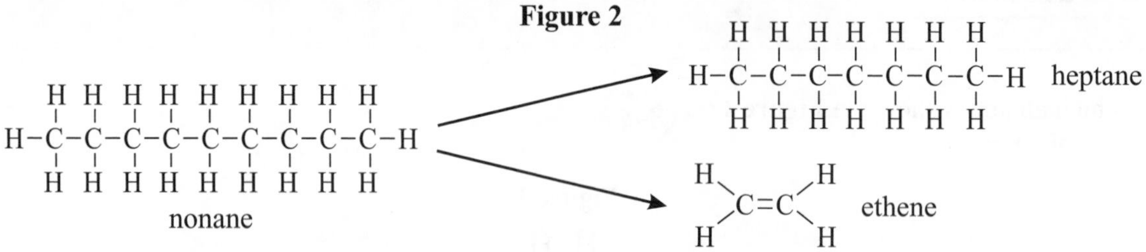

5.1 Complete the chemical equation for the cracking of nonane to make heptane and ethene.

$$C_9H_{20} \rightarrow \text{...................} + \text{...................}$$

[1 mark]

5.2 Samples of heptane and ethene were added to two separate test tubes of bromine water and shaken. Describe what you would expect to happen in each case.

[2 marks]

6 Crude oil can be separated into a number of different compounds in a fractional distillation column. **Figure 3** shows a fractional distillation column.

Figure 3

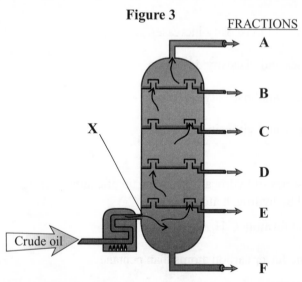

FRACTIONS

A

B

C

D

E

F

Crude oil

X

6.1 Which letter, **A-F**, represents the liquefied petroleum gas (LPG) fraction?

[1 mark]

6.2 The crude oil is heated until it becomes a gas and then enters the column at point **X** on **Figure 3**. The gas moves through the column and different fractions exit at different points. Explain why fractions with longer hydrocarbon chains exit near the bottom of the column.

[3 marks]

Revision Summary for Topic 7

Well, that's it for Topic 7, time to see how much of it you've taken in.
- Try these questions and tick off each one when you get it right.
- When you've done all the questions under a heading and are completely happy with it, tick it off.

Hydrocarbons (p.107-108) ☑

1) What two elements do hydrocarbons contain? ☑
2) True or False? Alkanes are the simplest type of hydrocarbon. ☑
3) Give the formula of propane. ☑
4) Draw the displayed formula of butane. ☑
5) What happens to the boiling point of hydrocarbons as the length of the hydrocarbon chain increases? ☑
6) What two waste products form from the complete combustion of hydrocarbons? ☑

Crude Oil (p.109-112) ☑

7) What did crude oil form from? ☑
8) Why is crude oil said to be a finite resource? ☑
9) True or False? Fractional distillation is used to separate the hydrocarbons in crude oil. ☑
10) Where do the shortest carbon chains condense in a fractional distillation column? ☑
11) Why is cracking used? ☑
12) What type of product produced by cracking is used for making polymers? ☑
13) What is used to test for alkenes? ☑
14) What kind of reaction is cracking? ☑
15) How is catalytic cracking carried out? ☑

Purity and Formulations

In a perfect world, every compound a chemist made would be <u>pure</u>. Unfortunately, in the real world it <u>doesn't</u> always work out like that. Luckily, there are ways to find out <u>how pure</u> a substance is.

Purity Has a **Different** Meaning in **Chemistry** to **Everyday**

1) <u>Usually</u> when you say that a <u>substance</u> is <u>pure</u> you mean that <u>nothing</u> has been <u>added</u> to it. So it's in its <u>natural state</u>. For example: pure milk or beeswax.

2) In <u>chemistry</u>, a pure substance is something that only contains <u>one compound</u> or <u>element</u> all the way through. It's <u>not mixed</u> with anything else.

The **Boiling** or **Melting Point** Tells You How **Pure** a Substance Is

1) A chemically pure substance will <u>melt</u> or <u>boil</u> at a <u>specific</u> temperature.

2) You can test how pure a known substance is by measuring its <u>melting</u> or <u>boiling point</u>. You then compare this value with the melting or boiling point of the <u>pure substance</u>. You can find this in a <u>data book</u>.

3) The <u>closer</u> your measured value is to the actual melting or boiling point, the <u>purer</u> your sample is.

4) Impurities in your sample will <u>lower</u> the <u>melting point</u>. They may also cause the sample to melt across a wider <u>range</u> of temperatures.

5) Impurities in your sample will <u>increase</u> the <u>boiling point</u>. They may also cause the sample to boil across a <u>range</u> of temperatures.

A **Formulation** is a **Mixture** with **Exact Amounts** of its **Parts**

1) <u>Formulations</u> are useful mixtures that have been designed for a <u>particular use</u>.

2) They are made by following a 'formula' (a recipe).

3) Each part of a formulation is <u>measured carefully</u> so that it's there in the <u>right amount</u>. This makes sure the formulation has right <u>properties</u> for it to work as it's supposed to.

Take a look at p.25 for more on mixtures.

> For example, <u>paints</u> are formulations.
> They are made up of:
> * <u>Pigment</u> — gives the paint colour.
> * <u>Solvent</u> — used to dissolve the other parts and change how runny the paint is.
> * <u>Binder</u> — holds the pigment in place after it's been painted on.
> * <u>Additives</u> — added to change the properties of the paint.
> The <u>chemicals</u> used and their <u>amounts</u> can be changed so the paint made is right for the job.

4) In <u>everyday life</u>, formulations can be found in cleaning products, fuels, medicines, cosmetics, fertilisers, metal alloys and even food and drink.

Make sure you can use data to identify pure and impure substances...

Knowing if a product is <u>pure</u> is really important for making things such as medicines or food. Extra stuff in it by mistake could change the <u>properties</u> of the product, and even make it <u>dangerous</u>.

Paper Chromatography

You met chromatography on page 26. Now it's time to see how it works.

Chromatography uses Two Phases

1) Chromatography is a method used to separate the substances in a mixture.

2) It can then be used to identify the substances.

3) The type of chromatography you need to know about is paper chromatography.
Like all types of chromatography, it has two 'phases'.
- A mobile phase — where the molecules can move.
In paper chromatography, this is a solvent (e.g. water or ethanol).
- A stationary phase — where the molecules can't move.
In paper chromatography, this is the paper.

4) During paper chromatography the solvent moves up the paper.
As the solvent moves, it carries the substances in the mixture with it.

The method for carrying out paper chromatography is on page 26.

5) In a chromatography experiment, the amount of time a chemical spends dissolved in the solvent or stuck on the paper is called its 'distribution'.

6) The more soluble a chemical is, the more time it spends dissolved in the solvent.
This means that the chemical will move further up the paper.

7) Different chemicals may be dissolved in the solvent for different amounts of time.
So the different chemicals will move different distances up the paper.

8) This means they separate into different spots.

Chromatography revision — it's a phase you have to get through...

Chromatography works because each of the chemicals in a mixture spends different amounts of time dissolved in the mobile phase and stuck to the stationary phase. It's great — all you need is some paper and a bit of solvent. There's more about using it to identify chemicals coming up on the next few pages.

PRACTICAL Interpreting Chromatograms

Now that you know a bit of the theory behind how paper chromatography works, here's how you can use a chromatogram to analyse a particular substance and find out what's in it.

The **Result** of Chromatography is Shown on a **Chromatogram**

1) Chromatograms show the result of chromatography experiments.

2) The solvent front is the furthest point reached by the solvent during a chromatography experiment.

3) Chemicals move different distances up the paper. So different spots show different chemicals.

4) The number of spots on a chromatogram is the smallest possible number of chemicals in the mixture.

5) Sometimes more than one chemical may travel the same distance up the paper. This means that these chemicals will only form one spot between them.

6) If you repeat the experiment with a different solvent, you'll get a different chromatogram. The spots may have travelled different distances compared to the solvent front. There might also be a different number of spots on the chromatogram.

7) If you only get one spot in lots of different solvents, there's only one chemical in the substance. This means the substance is pure.

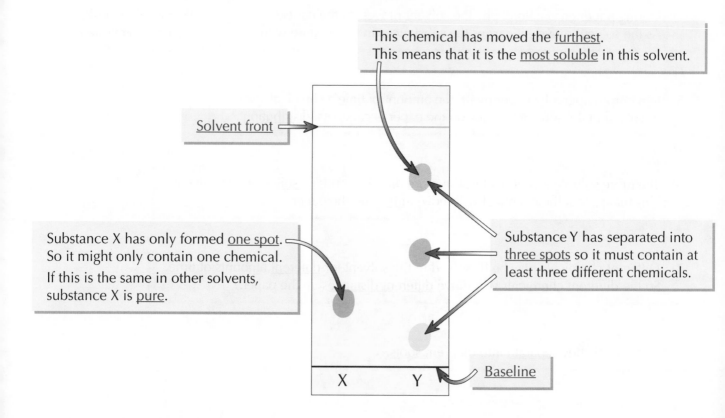

This chemical has moved the furthest.
This means that it is the most soluble in this solvent.

Solvent front

Substance X has only formed one spot.
So it might only contain one chemical.
If this is the same in other solvents,
substance X is pure.

Substance Y has separated into three spots so it must contain at least three different chemicals.

Baseline

X   Y

A pure substance will only ever produce one spot

PRACTICAL TIP

When you're doing paper chromatography, you might end up with a spot left sitting on the baseline, even after your solvent has run all the way up the paper. Any substance that stays on the baseline is insoluble in that solvent. If this happens, you could try the experiment using a different solvent, and see if the mystery substance dissolves in it.

Interpreting Chromatograms

If you were sad the last page on <u>chromatography</u> was finished — fear not. There's more to come on this page.

You can Calculate the R_f Value for Each Chemical

1) An <u>R_f value</u> is the <u>ratio</u> between the distance travelled by the <u>dissolved substance</u> and the distance travelled by the <u>solvent</u>.

2) The <u>further</u> a substance moves through the stationary phase, the <u>larger</u> the R_f value.

3) You can calculate R_f values using the formula:

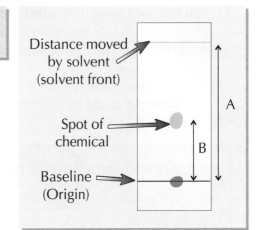

$$R_f = \frac{\text{distance moved by substance (B)}}{\text{distance moved by solvent (A)}}$$

— This is the distance from the baseline to the centre of the spot.

 **EXAMPLE:** **A chromatography experiment looking at the colours in a dye produces the chromatogram shown on the right. Calculate the R_f value for the red spot.**

1) Measure the <u>distance</u> moved by the <u>red spot</u> (B). This is the distance from the baseline to the centre of the spot. **29 mm**

2) Measure the <u>distance</u> moved by the <u>solvent</u> (A). **41 mm**

3) Calculate the <u>R_f value</u>.

$$R_f = \frac{\text{distance moved by substance (B)}}{\text{distance moved by solvent (A)}} = \frac{29}{41} = 0.70731... = 0.71$$

Give your answer to the smallest number of significant figures in the calculation.

4) The R_f value of a chemical will <u>change</u> if you change the <u>solvent</u>.

 MATHS TIP

You need to learn the formula for R_f

R_f values always lie <u>between 0 and 1</u>, as the <u>solvent</u> always <u>travels further</u> than any of the substances in the mixture. If you work out an R_f value to be outside this range, you know you've gone wrong somewhere (e.g. you may have written the fraction in the formula <u>upside-down</u>).

PRACTICAL — Interpreting Chromatograms

Time for one last page on chromatography — this one's all about using <u>references</u> to identify substances.

You Can **Identify Substances** in Mixtures Using Chromatography

1) You can use chromatography to see if a mixture <u>contains</u> a certain substance.

2) To do this, you run a <u>pure sample</u> of that substance (a <u>reference</u>) next to the mixture.

3) If the R_f value of the reference compound <u>matches</u> one of the spots in the mixture, the substance <u>could</u> be in the mixture. For example:

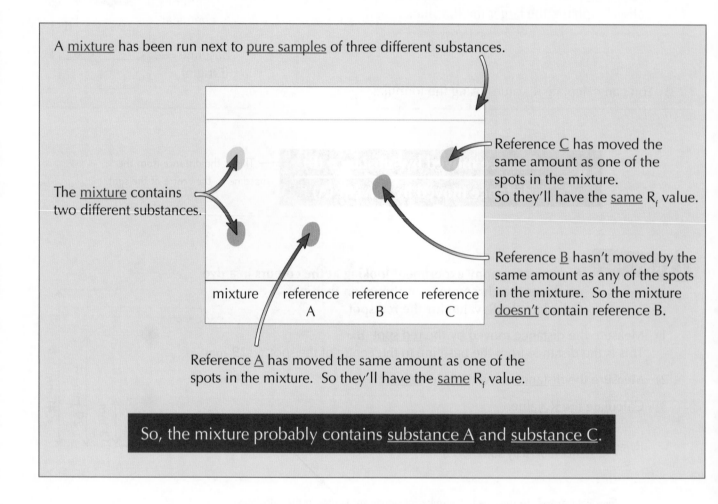

A <u>mixture</u> has been run next to <u>pure samples</u> of three different substances.

The <u>mixture</u> contains two different substances.

Reference <u>C</u> has moved the same amount as one of the spots in the mixture. So they'll have the <u>same</u> R_f value.

Reference <u>B</u> hasn't moved by the same amount as any of the spots in the mixture. So the mixture <u>doesn't</u> contain reference B.

mixture   reference A   reference B   reference C

Reference <u>A</u> has moved the same amount as one of the spots in the mixture. So they'll have the <u>same</u> R_f value.

So, the mixture probably contains <u>substance A</u> and <u>substance C</u>.

4) If the R_f values <u>match</u> in one solvent, you can <u>check</u> to see if the chemicals are the same by repeating with a <u>different solvent</u>. If they match again, it's <u>likely</u> that they're the <u>same</u>.

Reference spots are pure samples of known substances

Chromatography can be a bit tricky to get your head around sometimes, especially when you're given a chromatogram that contains quite a few different <u>spots</u>. Make sure you're really comfortable with how to use a chromatogram to <u>work out</u> what compounds are <u>present</u> in a <u>mixture</u>. It'll be worth it come the exam.

Tests for Gases

Yep, that's right, you need to revise tests for your test. There are a few ways to <u>test for gases</u>, but you only need to know these <u>four</u>. And two of them use fire. Pretty cool.

There are **Tests** for **Four Common Gases**

1) **Chlorine**

Chlorine <u>bleaches</u> damp <u>litmus paper</u>, turning it white.

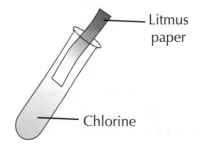

Litmus paper

Chlorine

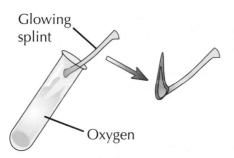

Glowing splint

Oxygen

2) **Oxygen**

If you put a glowing splint inside a test tube containing <u>oxygen</u>, the oxygen will <u>relight</u> the <u>glowing splint</u>.

3) **Carbon Dioxide**

You can test for carbon dioxide by bubbling it through a solution of <u>calcium hydroxide</u>.
If the gas is carbon dioxide, the solution will turn <u>cloudy</u>.
You can also do this test by <u>shaking</u> the gas with the solution.

Calcium hydroxide solution is also called limewater.

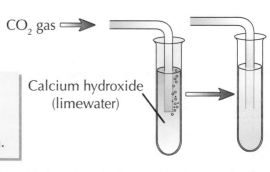

CO_2 gas

Calcium hydroxide (limewater)

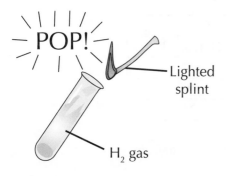

POP!

Lighted splint

H_2 gas

4) **Hydrogen**

If you hold a <u>lit splint</u> at the open end of a test tube containing hydrogen, you'll get a "<u>squeaky pop</u>".

PRACTICAL TIP

These are all really useful tests to know...

The method you use to <u>collect a gas</u> will depend on whether it's <u>lighter</u> or <u>heavier</u> than <u>air</u>. If it's <u>heavier</u> (like chlorine), you have the test tube the <u>right way up</u> and the gas will <u>sink</u> to the bottom. If it's <u>lighter</u> (like hydrogen), you have the test tube <u>upside-down</u> and the gas will <u>rise</u> to fill it.

Warm-Up & Exam Questions

Look, a chromatography question — those things are fun. Get your detective hat on and get stuck in...

1) What effect will impurities in a substance have on its boiling point?
2) Give an example of a formulation used in everyday life.
3) What effect does chromatography have on a mixture?
4) True of False? In chromatography, an R_f value represents the ratio between the distance travelled by two dissolved substances.

Exam Questions

1 Draw **one** line from each gas to the correct result of the test for that gas.

Gas	**Result**
Hydrogen	Turns damp litmus paper white
	Relights a glowing splint
Chlorine	Produces a "squeaky pop" with a lit splint
Carbon dioxide	Turns a solution of calcium hydroxide cloudy

[3 marks]

2 A scientist is preparing a formulation that contains only pure substances.
She measures the melting point of three substances, **A** – **C**. Her results are shown in **Table 1**.

Table 1

	Melting point (°C)	
Substance	**Experimental**	**Data book**
A	14	17
B	49	49
C	21 – 24	24

Which of the substances could the scientist use in her formulation? Tick **one** box.

☐ Substance B only   ☐ Substance A and C

☐ Substance C only   ☐ Substance A, B and C

[1 mark]

Exam Questions

3   Different groups of seaweed contain different types of a pigment called chlorophyll.
Table 2 shows which types of chlorophyll each group of seaweed contains.
Figure 1 shows the results of a chromatography experiment to analyse an unknown seaweed.

Table 2

Group of seaweed	Type of chlorophyll		
	a	b	c
Red	✓		
Brown	✓		✓
Green	✓	✓	

Use **Table 2** and **Figure 1** to identify which
group the unknown seaweed belongs to.

[1 mark]

Figure 1

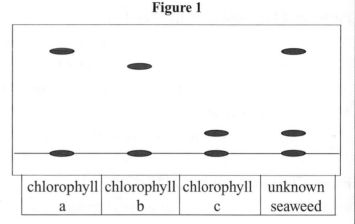

chlorophyll a	chlorophyll b	chlorophyll c	unknown seaweed

4   A scientist used chromatography to study the compounds present in five food colourings.
Four of the colourings were unknown (**A – D**). The other colouring was sunrise yellow.
The results are shown in **Figure 2**.

Figure 2

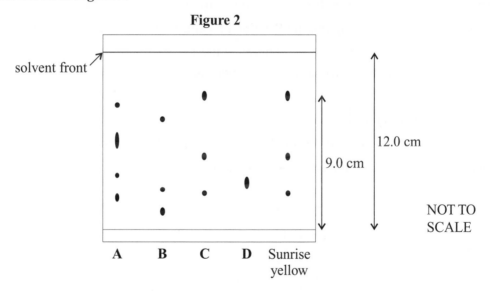

solvent front

12.0 cm

9.0 cm

NOT TO
SCALE

A   B   C   D   Sunrise
yellow

4.1   Which food colouring contained the compound that had the strongest attraction to the stationary phase?
[1 mark]

4.2   Which of the food colourings, **A-D**, could be the same as sunrise yellow?

[1 mark]

4.3   The R_f value of a spot can be calculated using the following formula:

$$R_f = \frac{\text{distance moved by substance}}{\text{distance moved by solvent}}$$

Calculate the R_f value for the spot of chemical in sunrise yellow
which is furthest up the chromatogram.

[2 marks]

Revision Summary for Topic 8

Here are some questions to work through before you get all geared up for Topic 9.
When you're done you should know a fair bit about how you can analyse the <u>components</u> of substances.
- Try these questions and <u>tick off each one</u> when you <u>get it right</u>.
- When you've done <u>all the questions</u> under a heading and are <u>completely happy</u> with it, tick it off.

Purity and Formulations (p.116) ☑

1) In chemistry, what does it mean if a substance is pure? ☑
2) What effect will impurities in a substance have on its melting point? ☑
3) Describe how you could use the boiling point of a substance to test whether it is pure. ☑
4) What is a formulation? ☑
5) Why do the different parts of a formulation need to be measured exactly? ☑

Paper Chromatography (p.117-120) ☑

6) What are the two phases called in chromatography? ☑
7) What is the solvent front on a chromatogram? ☑
8) What is the minimum number of compounds present in a sample
   that produces three spots in a chromatography experiment? ☑
9) A substance only produces one spot on a chromatogram in different solvents.
   What does this tell you about the purity of the substance? ☑
10) Give the formula for working out the R_f value of a substance. ☑
11) What will happen to the R_f value of a chemical if you
    change the solvent in the chromatography experiment? ☑

Tests for Gases (p.121) ☑

12) What colour does litmus paper turn in the presence of chlorine gas? ☑
13) How can you test if a gas in a test tube is oxygen? ☑

The Evolution of the Atmosphere

Theories for how the Earth's atmosphere <u>evolved</u> have changed a lot over the years. It's hard to gather evidence from such a <u>long time period</u> and from <u>so long ago</u> (4.6 billion years). Here's one idea we've got:

Phase 1 — **Volcanoes** Gave Out **Gases**

1) In the first <u>billion years</u> of the Earth's lifetime, its surface was covered in <u>volcanoes</u>.

2) These erupted and released lots of gases.
Scientists think these gases formed the <u>early atmosphere</u>.

3) The early atmosphere was probably mostly <u>carbon dioxide</u> (CO_2).
There was <u>little</u> or <u>no oxygen</u>.

4) This is quite like the atmospheres of <u>Mars</u> and <u>Venus</u> today.

5) Volcanoes also released <u>nitrogen</u> (this built up in the atmosphere over time),
<u>water vapour</u> and small amounts of <u>methane</u> and <u>ammonia</u>.

6) The <u>oceans</u> formed when the <u>water vapour</u> in the early atmosphere <u>condensed</u> (turned to liquid).

Phase 2 — **Oceans**, **Algae** and **Green Plants** Absorbed CO_2

1) Over time, much of the carbon dioxide (CO_2) was <u>removed</u> from the atmosphere.

2) Lots of the carbon dioxide <u>dissolved</u> in the oceans.

3) The dissolved carbon dioxide formed <u>carbonates</u> that precipitated as small, solid particles (<u>sediments</u>).

Precipitation is the formation of an insoluble solid from a solution.

4) When <u>green plants</u> and <u>algae</u> evolved, they took in some carbon dioxide during <u>photosynthesis</u> (see next page).

Before volcanic activity, the Earth didn't even have an atmosphere

One way scientists can get information about what Earth's <u>atmosphere</u> was like in the past is from <u>Antarctic ice cores</u>. Each year a layer of <u>ice</u> forms with tiny <u>bubbles of air</u> trapped in it. The <u>deeper</u> you go in the ice, the <u>older</u> the air. So analysing bubbles from different layers shows you how the atmosphere has <u>changed</u>.

The Evolution of the Atmosphere

Some **Carbon** Became **Trapped** in **Fossil Fuels** and **Rocks**

Some of the carbon that organisms took in from the atmosphere and oceans
became locked up in <u>rocks</u> and <u>fossil fuels</u> after the organisms died.

1) When sea organisms <u>die</u>, they fall to the seabed and get <u>buried</u>.
   Over millions of years, they're <u>squashed</u> down.
   This forms <u>sedimentary rocks</u> (e.g. coal and limestone), <u>oil</u> and <u>gas</u>.
   The carbon gets trapped within them.

2) Things like coal, crude oil and natural gas that are made this way are called '<u>fossil fuels</u>'.

3) <u>Crude oil</u> and <u>natural gas</u> are formed from the remains of <u>plankton</u> that settled on the seabed.

4) <u>Coal</u> is made from thick layers of <u>plants</u> that died and then settled on the seabed.

5) <u>Limestone</u> is mostly made of <u>calcium carbonate</u> from the <u>shells</u> and <u>skeletons</u> of marine organisms.

Phase 3 — Green Plants and Algae **Produced Oxygen**

1) Algae evolved about <u>2.7 billion</u> years ago.
   Then green plants evolved over the next <u>billion years</u> or so.

2) Green plants and algae produce <u>oxygen</u> in a reaction called <u>photosynthesis</u>:

> carbon dioxide + water $\xrightarrow{\text{light}}$ glucose + oxygen
>
> $$6CO_2 + 6H_2O \longrightarrow C_6H_{12}O_6 + 6O_2$$

3) Over time, oxygen levels <u>built up</u> in the atmosphere. This meant that animals could <u>evolve</u>.

4) The <u>proportions</u> of gases in the atmosphere have been similar for about the last <u>200 million years</u>.
   It is made up of about:

- 80% ($^4/_5$) <u>nitrogen</u>,
- 20% ($^1/_5$) <u>oxygen</u>,
- small amounts (<u>less than 1%</u>) of <u>other gases</u>
  (mainly carbon dioxide, noble gases and water vapour).

REVISION TIP

Not too much CO$_2$ and enough O$_2$ — perfect for life on Earth

You need to know the <u>rough proportions</u> of the gases in Earth's atmosphere, so don't just skip over
the numbers — you could get asked about them in the exam. Make sure you know that <u>nitrogen</u>
is <u>80%</u>, oxygen is <u>20%</u> and <u>everything else</u> makes up <u>less than 1%</u> of our atmosphere.

Climate Change and Greenhouse Gases

Greenhouse gases are important but can also cause <u>problems</u> — it's all about keeping a delicate <u>balance</u>.

Carbon Dioxide is a Greenhouse Gas

1) Greenhouse gases include <u>carbon dioxide</u>, <u>methane</u> and <u>water vapour</u>.
2) Greenhouse gases keep the Earth <u>warm</u> enough to support <u>life</u>. Here's how they work:

> 1) The <u>Sun</u> gives out <u>short wavelength</u> radiation.

> 2) This radiation is <u>reflected</u> back by the Earth as <u>long wavelength</u> radiation. This is <u>thermal</u> (heat) radiation. It's then <u>absorbed</u> by <u>greenhouse gases</u>.

Thermal radiation heats things up.

> 3) Greenhouse gases then give out this radiation in <u>all directions</u>.

> 4) Some radiation heads back towards the <u>Earth</u> and <u>warms up</u> the surface. This is the <u>greenhouse effect</u>.

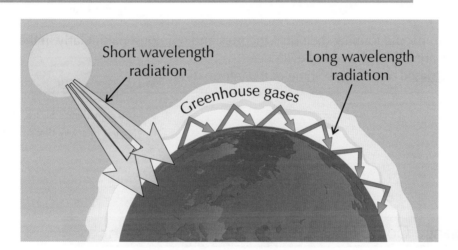

3) Some forms of <u>human activity</u> increase the amount of greenhouse gases in the atmosphere. For example:

> 1) <u>Deforestation</u>: fewer trees means that less carbon dioxide is taken in for <u>photosynthesis</u>.
>
> 2) Burning <u>fossil fuels</u>: <u>releases</u> carbon dioxide.
>
> 3) <u>Agriculture</u>: more <u>farm animals</u> produce more <u>methane</u> when they digest their food.
>
> 4) <u>Creating waste</u>: more <u>landfill sites</u> and more waste from <u>farming</u> means more carbon dioxide and methane is released when the waste breaks down.

Greenhouse gases aren't all bad news — we need them to survive

Without greenhouse gases our planet would be incredibly <u>cold</u> — the greenhouse effect warms the Earth enough for it to support <u>living things</u>. Without it we wouldn't be here. But the overall <u>balance</u> of gases in the atmosphere matters — you can have too much of a good thing, as you're about to find out...

Topic 9 — Chemistry of the Atmosphere

Climate Change and Greenhouse Gases

Increasing Carbon Dioxide is Linked to Climate Change

1) Recently, the average temperature of the Earth's surface has been <u>going up</u>.

2) Most scientists think this has been caused by the extra carbon dioxide from <u>human activity</u>.

3) They believe this will lead to <u>climate change</u>.

4) Evidence for this has been <u>peer-reviewed</u> (see page 2).
   This means that the information is <u>reliable</u>.

5) However, the Earth's climate is very <u>complex</u>.
   So, it's very hard to make a <u>model</u> that isn't <u>oversimplified</u>.

See page 3 for more on science in the media.

6) This has led to people forming their own <u>theories</u> and <u>opinions</u>, particularly in the <u>media</u>.
   These stories aren't based on good evidence —
   they may be <u>biased</u> or only give <u>some</u> of the information.

If something's biased, it favours one point of
view in a way that's not backed up by facts.

Climate Change Could Have Dangerous Consequences

1) Higher global temperature could cause <u>ice</u> in the Arctic and Antarctic to <u>melt</u> —
   causing <u>sea levels</u> to <u>rise</u>. This could lead to <u>more flooding</u>.

2) Changes in <u>rainfall</u> may cause some regions to get <u>too much</u> or <u>too little</u> water.

3) <u>Storms</u> may become more <u>frequent</u> and <u>severe</u>.

4) Changes in <u>temperature</u> and <u>rainfall</u> may affect the <u>production of food</u> in certain places.

People can get quite hot under the collar talking about all this...

That's because climate change could have a massive impact on many people's lives. So it's very
important to recognise when results might be <u>biased</u> or changed in favour of <u>one particular view</u>.
Data should always be <u>checked</u> and <u>peer-reviewed</u> before any final conclusions are made.

Carbon Footprints

Many scientists believe that greenhouse gas emissions from <u>human activities</u> are causing <u>climate change</u>. Knowing what things release lots of carbon dioxide could help <u>stop</u> climate change from happening.

Carbon Footprints are Tricky to Measure

1) Carbon footprints are a <u>measure</u> of the amount of <u>carbon dioxide</u> and other <u>greenhouse gases</u> released over the <u>full life cycle</u> of something. That can be almost <u>anything</u>:
   - a service (e.g. the school bus).
   - an event (e.g. the Olympics).
   - a product (e.g. a toastie maker).

2) <u>Measuring</u> the total carbon footprint of something can be <u>really hard</u> or even <u>impossible</u>.

3) But a <u>rough calculation</u> can give a good idea of what things release the <u>most</u> greenhouse gases. So, people can then <u>avoid using them</u> in the future.

There are Ways of Reducing Carbon Footprints

1) You can reduce a carbon footprint by <u>reducing</u> the amount of <u>greenhouse gases</u> given out by a process.

2) Here are some things that can be done:

- Using <u>renewable energy sources</u> (sources that won't run out) or <u>nuclear energy</u> instead of <u>fossil fuels</u>.
- Using <u>processes</u> that use <u>less energy</u> or produces less <u>waste</u> (decomposing waste releases methane).
- Governments could <u>tax</u> companies or individuals based on the amount of greenhouse gases they <u>emit</u>. This could encourage people to use processes which use less fuel and are <u>less polluting</u>.
- Governments can also put a <u>limit</u> on emissions of <u>all</u> greenhouse gases that companies make. They can then <u>sell licences</u> for emissions <u>up to</u> that cap.
- There's also technology that <u>captures</u> carbon dioxide <u>before</u> it's released into the atmosphere. This carbon dioxide is then <u>stored deep underground</u>.

But Making Reductions is Still Difficult

1) Reducing greenhouse gas emissions <u>isn't</u> simple.
2) <u>Alternative technologies</u> that release <u>less</u> carbon dioxide still need a lot of work.
3) Many <u>governments</u> are worried that making these changes will affect the <u>economies</u> of communities. This could be <u>bad</u> for people's <u>well-being</u> — especially those in <u>developing</u> countries.
4) This makes it hard for countries to <u>agree</u> to reduce emissions.
5) <u>Individuals</u> in developed countries also need to make changes to their <u>lifestyles</u>. But this is tricky when some <u>don't want to</u> and others don't understand <u>why</u> the changes are important or <u>how</u> to make them.

Air Pollution

Increasing carbon dioxide is causing climate change. But CO_2 isn't the only gas released when fossil fuels burn — you can also get other nasty gases like <u>oxides of nitrogen</u>, <u>sulfur dioxide</u> and <u>carbon monoxide</u>.

Combustion of Fossil Fuels Releases Gases and Particles

1) <u>Fossil fuels</u>, such as crude oil and coal, contain <u>hydrocarbons</u> (see page 107).

2) Hydrocarbons can <u>combust</u> (burn in oxygen). There are two types of combustion:

There's more about complete combustion on p.108.

<u>Complete combustion</u> — when there's <u>plenty</u> of oxygen around <u>all</u> of the fuel burns.

<u>Incomplete combustion</u> — when there's <u>not</u> enough oxygen around some of the fuel <u>does not</u> burn.

3) Both types of combustion release carbon dioxide and water vapour into the <u>atmosphere</u>.

4) During incomplete combustion, <u>solid particles</u> (called <u>particulates</u>) of soot (carbon) and <u>unburnt fuel</u> are also released. <u>Carbon monoxide</u> gas is also produced.

5) Particulates in the air and carbon monoxide can cause all sorts of <u>problems</u>:

Particulates

1) If particulates are <u>breathed in</u>, they can get stuck in the <u>lungs</u> and cause <u>damage</u>. This can lead to <u>respiratory</u> (breathing) <u>problems</u>.

2) They're also bad for the <u>environment</u> — they <u>reflect</u> sunlight back into space. This means that <u>less light</u> reaches the Earth — causing <u>global dimming</u>.

Carbon Monoxide

1) Carbon monoxide (CO) is really <u>dangerous</u> because it can stop your <u>blood</u> from <u>carrying enough oxygen</u> around the body.

2) A <u>lack</u> of oxygen in the blood can lead to <u>fainting</u>, a <u>coma</u> or <u>even death</u>.

3) Carbon monoxide doesn't have any <u>colour</u> or <u>smell</u>, so it's <u>very hard to detect</u>. This makes it even more <u>dangerous</u>.

Sulfur Dioxide and Oxides of Nitrogen Can be Released

1) Other pollutants are also released from <u>burning fossil fuels</u>.

2) <u>Sulfur dioxide</u> (SO_2) is released during the <u>combustion</u> of fossil fuels that contain <u>sulfur impurities</u>.

3) <u>Nitrogen oxides</u> form in a reaction between <u>nitrogen</u> and <u>oxygen</u> in the <u>air</u>. This reaction is caused by the <u>heat</u> of the burning fossil fuels.

4) These gases mix with <u>clouds</u> and cause <u>acid rain</u>.

5) Acid rain kills <u>plants</u>. It also <u>damages</u> buildings, statues and metals.

6) Sulfur dioxide and nitrogen oxides also cause <u>respiratory problems</u> if they're breathed in.

You can test for sulfur impurities in a fuel by bubbling the gases from combustion through a solution containing Universal indicator. If the fuel contains sulfur, the Universal indicator will turn red.

Fossil fuels are bad news — but we need them for many things...

...so a big reduction in their use is probably <u>hard</u> to achieve. Make sure you know the different <u>pollutants</u> that are given out when fuels burn, and the differences between <u>complete</u> and <u>incomplete</u> combustion.

Warm-Up & Exam Questions

There's lots of important information in this section, from the Earth's atmosphere to climate change and pollution. Answer these questions to see what you can remember and what you need to go over again.

Warm-Up Questions

1) Where do scientists think the gases that made up Earth's early atmosphere came from?
   A. Space   B. The ocean   C. Volcanoes   D. Burning fossil fuels
2) Give an example of a sedimentary rock.
3) Give an example of a fossil fuel.
4) True or false? Nuclear energy has a lower carbon footprint than burning fossil fuels.
5) Give one problem caused by sulfur dioxide in the atmosphere.

Exam Questions

1   Green plants and algae had a significant effect on Earth's early atmosphere.

1.1   Use words from the box to complete the sentences below.

> oxygen   carbon   carbon dioxide   particulates   nitrogen

When green plants first evolved, the Earth's atmosphere was mostly .... gas .

These plants produced .... by the process of photosynthesis.

Some of the .... from dead plants eventually became 'locked up' in fossil fuels.

[3 marks]

1.2   Complete the balanced symbol equation for photosynthesis.

$$6 \text{.................} + \text{.........} H_2O \rightarrow C_6H_{12}O_6 + 6 \text{...................}$$

[2 marks]

1.3   Which line in **Table 1** shows the correct percentages of each gas in the Earth's atmosphere today?

Table 1

	Percentage in atmosphere (%)			
	Carbon dioxide	**Oxygen**	**Nitrogen**	**Water vapour**
A	20	70	10	less than 1
B	10	20	70	less than 1
C	less than 1	20	80	less than 1
D	less than 1	10	80	10

☐ A   ☐ B   ☐ C   ☐ D

[1 mark]

Exam Questions

2 Fossil fuels contain hydrocarbons. **(Grade 3-4)**

2.1 Which of the following is a fossil fuel?
Tick **one** box.

☐ Limestone   ☐ Natural gas   ☐ Carbon dioxide   ☐ Water

[1 mark]

When hydrocarbons burn without enough oxygen present,
solid particles and carbon monoxide can be produced.

2.2 Name the type of reaction that occurs when hydrocarbons burn in oxygen.

[1 mark]

2.3 What name is given to the solid particles that can be produced
when hydrocarbons burn without enough oxygen present?

[1 mark]

2.4 Describe **two** problems caused by these solid particles in the air.

[2 marks]

2.5 Give **two** reasons why carbon monoxide is difficult to detect.

[1 mark]

3 This question is about greenhouse gases and climate change. **(Grade 4-5)**

3.1 Which of the following is an example of a greenhouse gas?
Tick **one** box.

☐ Oxygen   ☐ Nitrogen   ☐ Methane   ☐ Argon

[1 mark]

3.2 Greenhouse gases absorb thermal radiation that has been reflected by the Earth.
Explain how this leads to global warming.

[3 marks]

3.3 Give **two** human activities that have increased the amount of greenhouse gases in Earth's atmosphere.

[2 marks]

3.4 Give **one** possible consequence of climate change.

[1 mark]

3.5 Describe **one** action that governments could take to try to
reduce the amount of greenhouse gases in the atmosphere.

[1 mark]

4* Earth's early atmosphere contained large amounts of carbon dioxide. **(Grade 4-5)**

Describe how the oceans, plants and algae removed some of this carbon dioxide,
and how this eventually led to the formation of coal.

[4 marks]

Revision Summary for Topic 9

That's all for Topic 9, but before you breathe a sigh of relief, there are some questions to get through.
- Try these questions and tick off each one when you get it right.
- When you've done all the questions under a heading and are completely happy with it, tick it off.

The Evolution of the Atmosphere (p.125-126) ☑

1) How did volcanoes help to form the early atmosphere? ☑
2) Name three of the gases that scientists think were present in the early atmosphere. ☑
3) Give one way that the levels of carbon dioxide in the early atmosphere were reduced. ☑
4) Name the gas produced during photosynthesis. ☑
5) What percentage of the Earth's atmosphere today is made up of carbon dioxide? ☑

Climate Change and Greenhouse Gases (p.127-128) ☑

6) Name two greenhouse gases. ☑
7) How do greenhouse gases help to support life on Earth? ☑
8) How does agriculture contribute towards climate change? ☑
9) Why is it difficult to make a model to investigate climate change? ☑

Carbon Footprints and Air Pollution (p.129-130) ☑

10) What is a carbon footprint? ☑
11) Give two things that can be done to reduce carbon footprints. ☑
12) Give one reason why reducing carbon dioxide emissions can be difficult. ☑
13) Why is carbon monoxide dangerous? ☑
14) Describe how the following air pollutants are produced:
    a) sulfur dioxide   b) nitrogen oxides. ☑
15) Describe how acid rain forms. ☑
16) State two problems caused by acid rain. ☑

Finite and Renewable Resources

There are lots of different resources that humans use for things like <u>electricity</u>, <u>heating</u>, <u>travelling</u>, <u>building materials</u> and <u>food</u>. Some of these resources can be replaced, some can't.

Natural Resources Come From the Earth, Sea and Air

1) <u>Natural resources</u> form by themselves — they're not made by <u>humans</u>.
   They include anything that comes from the earth, sea or air, e.g. cotton and oil.

2) Some natural products can be <u>replaced</u> or <u>improved</u> by man-made products or processes.
   For example:

   - <u>Rubber</u> is a natural product that comes from the sap of a tree.
     But we can now make <u>polymers</u> (see p.57) to <u>replace</u> some natural rubber to make things like tyres.
   - <u>Wool</u> is a natural product that comes from animals such as sheep. But scientists have developed <u>synthetic</u> (man-made) <u>fibres</u> that we can use instead of wool to make things like jumpers and blankets.

3) <u>Agriculture</u> (farming) helps to increase our supply of natural resources to <u>provide</u> food, timber, clothing and fuel. It also provides <u>conditions</u> which can make <u>natural resources</u> better for our needs.

   E.g. the development of <u>fertilisers</u> means we can increase the <u>amount</u> of crops grown in a given area.

Some Natural Resources will Run Out

1) <u>Renewable resources</u> can be remade at least as fast as we use them.

2) This means that they can be <u>replaced</u> fairly <u>quickly</u>.

   - For example, <u>timber</u> is a renewable resource.
     Trees can be <u>planted</u> following a harvest and only take a <u>few years</u> to regrow.
   - Other examples of renewable resources include <u>fresh water</u> and <u>food</u>.

3) <u>Finite</u> (non-renewable) <u>resources</u> are remade very <u>slowly</u> (or not at all).
   So we use them up <u>quicker</u> than we can replace them. This means that they'll eventually <u>run out</u>.

4) Finite resources include <u>fossil fuels</u> and <u>nuclear fuels</u>, as well as <u>minerals</u> and <u>metals</u> found in the ground.

5) We can <u>process</u> many finite resources to provide fuels and materials necessary for modern life.
   For example:

   - <u>Fractional distillation</u> (see p.110) is used to produce usable products such as petrol from crude oil.
   - Metal ores are <u>reduced</u> to produce <u>pure metals</u> (see p.80).

Natural resources can be renewable or finite

It's important that we're always able to get the resources we need to survive. Make sure you know the difference between a <u>finite</u> and a <u>renewable</u> resource and a few <u>examples</u> of each.

Resources and Sustainability

Tables, Charts and Graphs can Tell You About Different Resources

You can <u>interpret</u> information about resources from information that's given to you.

 **EXAMPLE:**

The table below shows how long it takes for three resources to form. The resources are coal, wood and cotton. Work out which resource is coal.

	Time it takes to form
Resource 1	10 years
Resource 2	120-180 days
Resource 3	10^6 years

Wood and cotton are both renewable resources.

Coal is a finite resource.

Finite resources take a very long time to form.

Resource 3 takes a much longer amount of time to form compared to Resources 1 and 2.

Coal is Resource 3.

10^6 is a quick way of showing 1 000 000. This is because $10^6 = 10 \times 10 \times 10 \times 10 \times 10 \times 10 = 1 000 000$.

We Need to Consider the Future When Choosing Resources

1) <u>Sustainable development</u> means thinking about the needs of <u>people today</u> without damaging the lives of <u>people in the future</u>.

2) Using, extracting and processing resources can be unsustainable. This could be because:

- Some resources are <u>non-renewable</u> — they'll run out one day. For example, the <u>raw materials</u> used to make metals, building materials, many plastics and things made from clay and glass are <u>limited</u>.

- Extraction processes can use lots of <u>energy</u> and produce lots of <u>waste</u>.

  Extraction processes separate the materials you want from the other things that they're mixed with.

- Turning resources into useful materials, like <u>glass</u> or <u>bricks</u>, often uses <u>energy</u> made from <u>finite resources</u>.

3) One way to be more sustainable is to use <u>fewer</u> finite resources. This reduces both the use of finite resources and anything needed to produce them.

4) We can do this by <u>reusing</u> and <u>recycling</u> materials when we're finished with them. During recycling, <u>waste</u> is <u>processed</u> so that it can be used to make <u>new products</u>.

There's more on reusing and recycling on the next page.

5) We can't stop using finite resources completely. But scientists can <u>develop</u> processes that use <u>less</u> and <u>reduce</u> damage to the environment.

We need to be responsible with resources that won't last forever

Sustainable development is talked about a lot these days, however it's often quite <u>hard</u> to achieve in practice. It can be a <u>difficult</u> topic, too — making the changes we need to isn't always easy and can have a big impact on many people's lives. Plus people <u>can't always agree</u> on the best thing to do.

Reuse and Recycling

Supplies of many materials used in the modern world are <u>limited</u>. Once they're finished with, it's usually far better to <u>recycle</u> them than to use new finite resources, which will run out.

Recycling Metals is Important

1) <u>Mining</u> and <u>extracting</u> metals takes lots of <u>energy</u>.
   Most of this energy comes from burning <u>fossil fuels</u>.

2) It's usually <u>better</u> to <u>recycle</u> metals instead of making new metals.

   <u>Benefits of recycling</u>:
   - It often uses much <u>less energy</u> than the amount needed to make a new metal.
   - It helps <u>save</u> some of the finite amount of each metal in the earth.
   - It cuts down on the amount of <u>waste</u> getting sent to <u>landfill</u>.

3) Metals can be recycled by <u>melting</u> them and then
   moulding (<u>recasting</u>) them into the shape of a new product.

4) Sometimes, different metals won't need to be completely <u>separated</u> before recycling.
   The amount of <u>separation</u> depends on what the final product will be.

   For example, waste steel and iron can be kept together.
   This is because they can both be added to iron in a <u>blast furnace</u>.
   This means that <u>less iron ore</u> will be needed.

   A blast furnace is used to extract iron from its ore at a high temperature using carbon.

Glass can be **Reused** or **Recycled**

1) <u>Reusing</u> or <u>recycling</u> glass can help <u>sustainability</u>.

2) This <u>reduces</u> the amount of <u>energy</u> used for making new glass.

3) It also means that <u>less</u> glass is thrown away, so less <u>waste</u> is produced.

   - <u>Glass bottles</u> can often be <u>reused</u> without reshaping.
   - Some glass products can't be reused so they're <u>recycled</u> for a different use instead.
   - The glass is <u>crushed</u> and <u>melted</u>. It's then reshaped to make other glass products like jars.

Recycling is key to sustainability — it's useful in lots of ways...

Remember that recycling doesn't just reduce the use of raw materials, it also reduces the amount of <u>energy</u> used, the amount of <u>damage</u> to the environment and the amount of <u>waste</u> that is produced.

Life Cycle Assessments

If a company wants to manufacture a new product, they carry out a life cycle assessment (LCA).

Life Cycle Assessments Show Total Environmental Costs

1) A life cycle assessment (LCA) looks at every stage of a product's life to assess the impact (effect) it would have on the environment.
2) Here are the four different stages:

1) Getting the Raw Materials

1) Lots of raw materials need to be extracted (separated from other materials) before we can use them for a product.
2) Extracting raw materials can damage the local environment, e.g. mining metals.
3) Extraction uses lots of energy. This can result in pollution.
4) Raw materials often need to be processed (e.g. by changing their shape and properties) to turn them into useful materials.
5) This often needs large amounts of energy. E.g. extracting metals from ores (see p.80 and 83) or fractional distillation of crude oil (see p.110).

2) Manufacture and Packaging

1) Making products and their packaging can use a lot of energy and other resources.
2) It can cause lots of pollution too.
3) Chemical reactions are sometimes used to make products. These reactions also produce waste products which need to be got rid of.
4) Some of this waste can be turned into other useful chemicals. This reduces the amount that ends up polluting the environment.

3) Using the Product

1) The use of a product can also damage the environment. See page 127 for more on greenhouse gases.
2) For example, burning fuels releases greenhouse gases and other harmful substances. Fertilisers can drain into streams and rivers, causing harm to plants and animals.
3) It's also important to think about how long a product is used for or how many uses it gets. Products that need lots of energy to produce but are used for ages mean less waste in the long run.

4) Product Disposal

1) Products are often thrown away in landfill sites.
2) This takes up space and pollutes land and water. For example, paint can wash off a product and get into rivers.
3) Energy is used to transport waste to landfill. This can release pollutants into the atmosphere, such as carbon monoxide (see p.130) and carbon dioxide.
4) Products might be incinerated (burnt), which causes air pollution.

LCAs look at the effect a product has on the environment

LCAs can show us how to improve products, so we can make them less damaging to the environment. However, LCAs can also be very time consuming and expensive, because there is so much to think about.

Life Cycle Assessments

You can compare the life cycle assessments of <u>similar products</u> to see which has the <u>smallest effect</u> on the environment. You might want to do this to see which material will affect the environment the <u>least</u>.

You Can **Compare** Life Cycle Assessments for **Plastic** and **Paper Bags**

1) You may be asked to <u>compare</u> life cycle assessment (LCA) information about <u>paper</u> and <u>plastic bags</u>.

2) You can then decide which type of bag is the <u>least harmful</u> to the environment.

Life Cycle Assessment Stage	Plastic Bag	Paper Bag
Raw Materials	Crude oil	Wood
Manufacturing and Packaging	Plastics are made from compounds extracted from crude oil by fractional distillation and processed by cracking and polymerisation. Waste is reduced as the other fractions of crude oil have other uses.	Pulped wood is processed using lots of energy. Lots of waste is made.
Using the Product	Can be reused several times. Can be used for other things as well as shopping. For example, as bin liners.	Usually only used once.
Product Disposal	Recyclable but many types aren't biodegradable. Take up space in landfill and pollute land.	Can be recycled. Biodegradable and non-toxic.

3) LCAs have shown that even though plastic bags <u>aren't</u> usually <u>biodegradable</u>, they may be <u>less harmful</u> to the environment.

4) This is because they take less energy to make and have a longer <u>lifespan</u> than paper bags.

If something's biodegradable, it can be broken down naturally by microorganisms (tiny living things like bacteria).

There are **Problems** with **Life Cycle Assessments**

1) It's quite easy to measure things like the use of <u>energy</u> or <u>resources</u>, and the <u>production</u> of some types of <u>waste</u>. So we can give all of these measurements a <u>number</u> in an LCA.

2) But measuring some effects is much <u>harder</u>.

- For example, plastic bags that litter the environment <u>don't</u> look very nice.
- But measuring how unattractive something looks isn't easy. The person measuring it has to use their own <u>judgement</u>.

3) So, producing an LCA can involve the feelings of the person carrying out the <u>assessment</u> as well as facts. So the results could change depending on who does the assessment. This means LCAs can be <u>biased</u>.

4) <u>Selective LCAs</u> only show <u>some</u> of the impacts that a product has on the environment. So these can also be <u>biased</u> because they can be written to purposely support the claims of a company. This would give the company <u>positive advertising</u>.

If something is biased, that means it favours one point of view in a way that isn't backed up by facts.

LCAs aren't all they are cracked up to be...

In the exam, you may have to <u>compare</u> LCAs for plastic and paper bags and decide which one is the <u>most environmentally friendly</u>. Each bag has good and bad points, but don't forget that <u>not all</u> environmental impacts can be measured in an LCA. Also, the results of an LCA can be <u>biased</u>.

Warm-Up & Exam Questions

That's some more revision done and dusted — now it's time to test yourself on how much you've taken in. Have a go at the questions on this page to see if you need to look back at some topics.

Warm-Up Questions

1) Give one example of a natural resource which has been replaced by a man-made alternative.
2) True or false? One way to be more sustainable is to use fewer finite resources.
3) Give two positive effects of recycling metals.
4) What is the purpose of a life cycle assessment?

Exam Questions

1 Natural resources are formed without human input and are used for construction, fuel and food.

1.1 What is a renewable natural resource?
Tick **one** box.

☐ A natural resource that can't be remade by humans.

☐ A natural resource that can be remade at least as fast as we use it.

☐ A natural resource that is only remade very slowly.

[1 mark]

1.2 Aluminium is used to make soft drink cans.
Extracting aluminium uses a large amount of energy.
Suggest **one** way that the use of soft drink cans can be made more sustainable.

[1 mark]

2 **Table 1** shows part of a life cycle assessment for two types of bag.

Table 1

	Raw materials	Manufacturing	Reusability	Disposal
Plastic bag	Crude oil	Waste from manufacturing process can be used to make other products.	Can be reused many times, in different ways.	Recyclable, but often not biodegradable. Many end up in landfill sites or the oceans.
Paper bag	Wood	High energy process that generates lots of waste.	Usually not reusable.	Can be recycled. Biodegradable and non-toxic.

2.1* Use the information in **Table 1** and your own knowledge to evaluate which type of bag is better for the environment.

[6 marks]

2.2 Give **two** reasons why a life cycle assessment may be biased.

[2 marks]

Potable Water and Water Treatment

We all need safe drinking water. The <u>way</u> that water's made safe depends on <u>local conditions</u>.

Potable Water is Water You Can Drink

1) <u>Potable water</u> is water that's <u>safe</u> for <u>humans to drink</u>. We need it to <u>live</u>.

2) Some water is <u>naturally</u> potable, but most water needs to be <u>treated</u> before it's safe to drink.

3) Potable water isn't <u>pure</u>. Pure water <u>only</u> contains H_2O molecules but <u>potable water</u> can contain lots of other <u>dissolved substances</u>.

See p.116 for more on purity.

4) For water to be safe to drink, it must:
   - not have <u>high levels</u> of <u>dissolved salts</u>,
   - have a <u>pH</u> between <u>6.5</u> and <u>8.5</u>,
   - not have any bad things in it (like <u>bacteria</u> or other <u>microbes</u>).

How Potable Water is Produced Depends on Where You Are

1) Fresh water is water that <u>doesn't</u> have much dissolved in it. Rainwater is a type of <u>fresh water</u>.

2) When it rains, water can either collect as <u>surface water</u> or as <u>ground water</u>.

   <u>Surface water</u>: collects in <u>lakes</u>, <u>rivers</u> and <u>reservoirs</u> (places for storing liquids).
   <u>Ground water</u>: collects in rocks that trap water underground.

3) When producing potable water, companies need to choose a <u>suitable</u> source of freshwater. In the UK, the <u>source</u> of fresh water used depends on <u>location</u>.

4) Surface water tends to <u>dry up</u> first. So in <u>warm areas</u>, such as the south-east, <u>most</u> of the water supply comes from <u>ground water</u>. This is because it is underground so <u>doesn't</u> dry up.

Most Fresh Water Needs to be Treated to Make it Safe

1) Fresh water contains <u>low levels</u> of dissolved substances.

2) It still needs to be <u>treated</u> to make it <u>safe</u> before we use it.

3) This process includes:

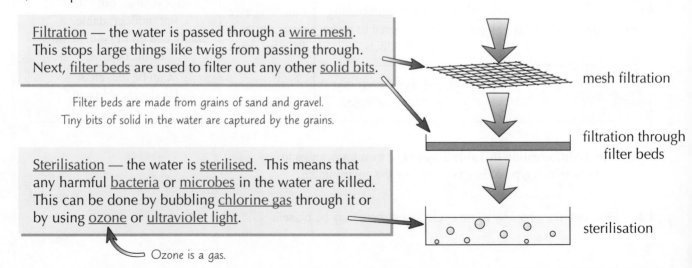

<u>Filtration</u> — the water is passed through a <u>wire mesh</u>. This stops large things like twigs from passing through. Next, <u>filter beds</u> are used to filter out any other <u>solid bits</u>.

Filter beds are made from grains of sand and gravel. Tiny bits of solid in the water are captured by the grains.

mesh filtration

filtration through filter beds

<u>Sterilisation</u> — the water is <u>sterilised</u>. This means that any harmful <u>bacteria</u> or <u>microbes</u> in the water are killed. This can be done by bubbling <u>chlorine gas</u> through it or by using <u>ozone</u> or <u>ultraviolet light</u>.

Ozone is a gas.

sterilisation

Potable Water and Water Treatment

Some countries have limited supplies of fresh water. They need to use other water sources, like the sea.

Potable Water Can Be Made From Seawater

1) In some very dry countries there's not enough surface or ground water.
So instead they use seawater to provide potable water.

2) Seawater contains salts which need to be removed before we can drink it.

3) These salts are removed by a process called desalination.

Distillation Can Be Used to Purify Seawater

1) Distillation can be used to remove the salt from seawater (desalination).

2) You can test and purify a sample of water in the lab using distillation:

Seawater can also be purified by a process called reverse osmosis (see next page).

1) Use a pH meter to test the pH of a sample of water (see p.76).
If the pH is too high or too low, you'll need to neutralise it (make it neutral).
You do this by adding some acid (if the sample's alkaline) or some alkali
(if the sample's acidic) until the pH is 7.

2) Set up the equipment as shown in the diagram below.

Neutral solutions are neither acidic nor alkaline. They have a pH of 7. E.g. pure water is neutral. There's more on this on page 74.

water out
condenser
round bottomed flask
salty water
cold water in
fresh water
Bunsen burner

3) Heat the water in the flask using a Bunsen burner.

4) As the water heats up, it becomes a gas (it evaporates).
The gas then enters the condenser as steam.
Cold water is pumped around the condenser to cool the steam inside of it.
This drop in temperature makes the steam condense back into liquid water.

5) Collect the water running out of the condenser in a beaker.

6) Retest the pH of the water with a pH meter to check it's neutral.

7) After the water has been distilled (all of the water has evaporated from the flask),
see whether there are any crystals in the round bottomed flask.
If there are crystals it means that there were salts in the water before you distilled it.

Potable Water and Water Treatment

You saw on the previous page how distillation can be used to purify seawater.
There's another method you need to know about — reverse osmosis.

Seawater can be Purified Using Reverse Osmosis

1) Seawater can be purified by processes that use thin layers of material called membranes. Membranes have really tiny holes that only let certain things pass through them.

2) One of these processes is called reverse osmosis. The salty water is passed through a membrane. The membrane lets water molecules pass through but traps the salts. This separates them from the water.

There's more on purifying seawater using distillation on the previous page.

3) Both distillation and reverse osmosis need loads of energy to work which makes them expensive. This is why they're not used when there are other sources of fresh water available.

Waste Water Comes from Lots of Different Sources

1) We use water for lots of things at home — like having a bath, going to the toilet and doing the washing-up. When you flush this water and other waste matter down the drain, it goes into the sewers forming sewage. The sewage is then carried by the sewers to sewage treatment plants.

2) Agricultural (farming) systems also produce a lot of waste water.

3) Waste water has to be treated before it can be put back into fresh water sources like rivers or lakes. This is to remove any pollutants such as organic matter and harmful microbes (e.g. bacteria and viruses) so that the water doesn't cause health problems.

4) Waste water from industrial processes also has to be collected and treated.

Organic matter contains carbon compounds that come from the remains and waste of organisms.

5) Industrial waste water can contain organic matter and harmful chemicals. So it needs further treatment before it's safe to put back into the environment.

The water that comes out of our taps has been treated

Location is a really important factor in determining how water is treated. For example, in the UK, there is a lot of fresh water available so this is filtered and then sterilised. However, in very dry countries a more expensive process may have to be used, such as the distillation or reverse osmosis of sea water.

Potable Water and Water Treatment

Dealing with waste water is really important to make sure we don't <u>pollute</u> our environment.

Sewage **Treatment** Happens in **Several Stages**

1) Some of the <u>processes</u> involved in treating waste water at sewage treatment plants are shown below.

1) Screening

The sewage is <u>screened</u> to remove any <u>large bits</u> of material (like twigs or plastic bags) and any <u>grit</u> (small bits of stone and sand).

2) Sedimentation

Then it goes through <u>sedimentation</u>. The <u>heavier</u> solids sink to the bottom to produce <u>sludge</u>. The lighter <u>effluent</u> (liquid waste) floats on the top.

4) Anaerobic Digestion

The <u>sludge</u> is also <u>broken down</u> by bacteria in a process called <u>anaerobic digestion</u>. This produces <u>methane gas</u> which can be used as an <u>energy source</u>. The remaining waste can be used as <u>fertiliser</u>.

3) Aerobic Digestion

The <u>effluent</u> is <u>removed</u> and treated by <u>biological aerobic digestion</u>. This is where <u>bacteria</u> break down any <u>organic matter</u> — including <u>other microbes</u> in the water.

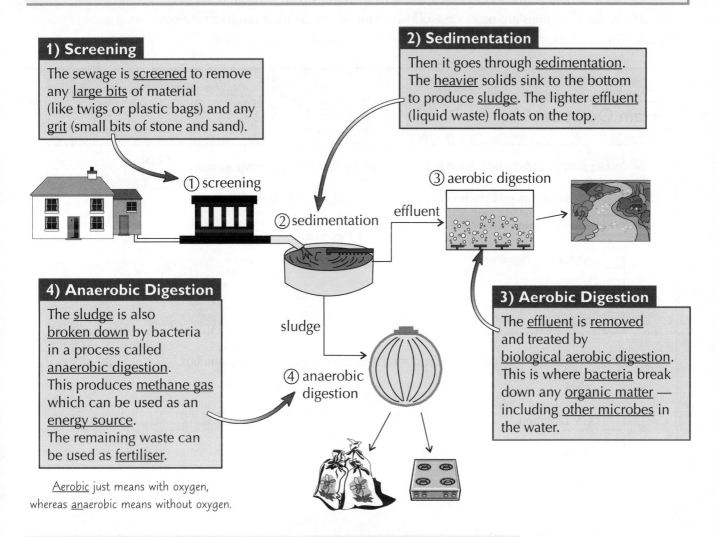

<u>Aerobic</u> just means with oxygen, whereas <u>an</u>aerobic means without oxygen.

2) Waste water containing <u>toxic substances</u> needs extra stages of treatment. This may include adding <u>chemicals</u>, <u>UV radiation</u> or using <u>membranes</u>.

3) Sewage treatment has <u>more stages</u> than treating <u>fresh water</u> but uses <u>less energy</u> than the <u>desalination</u> of <u>salt water</u>. So it could be used as an option in areas where there's not much fresh water. However, people don't like the idea of drinking water that used to be sewage.

Waste water can be recycled to produce potable water
To learn the stages of water treatment, <u>cover</u> the diagram, <u>write out</u> each step and then <u>check</u> it.

Warm-Up & Exam Questions

Now you know all there is to possibly know about water it's time to test yourself with some questions.

Warm-Up Questions

1) Describe one feature of potable water that makes it safe for drinking.
2) True or False? The first step in treating fresh water involves mesh filtration.
3) What two things are produced following the sedimentation stage of water treatment?
4) True or False? Sewage treatment has more stages than the treatment of fresh water.

Exam Questions

1 Waste water needs to be treated before it can be returned to the environment. **Grade 1-3**

1.1 What is the first step in the process of sewage treatment? Tick **one** box.

☐ Sedimentation

☐ Anaerobic digestion

☐ Aerobic digestion

☐ Screening

[1 mark]

1.2 What is used to break down sewage during anaerobic digestion? Tick **one** box.

☐ Acid

☐ UV radiation

☐ Bacteria

☐ Oxygen

[1 mark]

2 Fresh water can be treated to produce potable water. **Grade 3-4**

2.1 What is potable water?
Tick **one** box.

☐ Water that only contains H_2O molecules.

☐ Water with a pH above 9.

☐ Water that comes from the surface.

☐ Water that is safe to drink.

[1 mark]

2.2 Why is fresh water filtered during the production of potable water?

[1 mark]

2.3 Suggest **one** thing that could be used to sterilise the water during the sterilisation stage of the process.

[1 mark]

Exam Questions

3   A student wants to carry out distillation of a sample of seawater.
     Figure 2 shows the apparatus that the student is going to use.

Figure 2

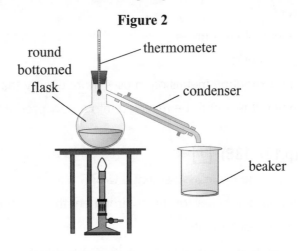

round
bottomed
flask
thermometer
condenser
beaker

3.1   Use an **X** to label the point on **Figure 2** where the pure water is collected.

[1 mark]

3.2   Describe how the processes of evaporation and condensation are used to obtain a sample of
      pure water from seawater.

[2 marks]

3.3   The sample of seawater has a high pH.
      Suggest **one** thing that the student could do to change the pH of the water so that it is safe to drink.

[1 mark]

3.4   How will the student know when all the water has been distilled?

[1 mark]

When the distillation was complete, the student noticed crystals in the round bottomed flask.

3.5   Explain why crystals formed in the flask at the end of the distillation.

[1 mark]

4   This question is about waste water.

4.1   Explain why waste water has to be treated before it can be returned to the environment.

[2 marks]

4.2   During the sedimentation step of sewage treatment, effluent and sludge are separated from each other.
      Describe how effluent and sludge are then treated before being returned to the environment.

[3 marks]

A factory makes cleaning products.

4.3   The factory's waste water needs more treatment than household waste water before it can
      be returned to the environment. Explain why.

[1 mark]

5   Membranes are thin layers of material that contain very small holes.

5.1   Explain how reverse osmosis uses membranes to purify seawater.

[2 marks]

5.2   Why is reverse osmosis an expensive process?

[1 mark]

Revision Summary for Topic 10

That wraps up <u>Topic 10</u> — time to try these questions to see if you've got this topic in the bag.
- Try these questions and <u>tick off each one</u> when you <u>get it right</u>.
- When you've done <u>all the questions</u> under a heading and are <u>completely happy</u> with it, tick it off.

Chemistry and Sustainability (p.134-136) ☑

1) What is a natural resource? ☑
2) Give two examples of renewable resources. ☑
3) What is sustainable development? ☑
4) True or False? Mining and extracting metals often uses more energy than recycling them. ☑
5) What happens to glass when it is sent to be recycled into a new product? ☑

Life Cycle Assessments (p.137-138) ☑

6) What are the four stages of a life cycle assessment (LCA)? ☑
7) Give one way that paper bags are better for the environment than plastic bags. ☑
8) What is a selective life cycle assessment? ☑
9) Why might companies want to use selective life cycle assessments? ☑

Potable Water and Water Treatment (p.140-143) ☑

10) True or False? Potable water is water that needs to be treated before it is safe to drink. ☑
11) True or False? Ground water collects in rivers and lakes. ☑
12) Name two processes you could use to purify sea water. ☑
13) Name two different sources of waste water. ☑
14) Give one example of a pollutant that might be found in waste water. ☑
15) What happens during the screening step of sewage treatment? ☑
16) Give one advantage of obtaining drinking water from the treatment of sewage, rather than the desalination of salt water. ☑

Taking Measurements

You've got a few <u>practicals</u> that you need to know about for your exams. This section is full of lots of information and advice for how to carry out practicals <u>really well</u>. First up — <u>measuring</u> things...

Mass Should Be Measured Using a Balance

1) To measure mass, put the <u>container</u> you're measuring the substance <u>into</u> on the <u>balance</u>.

2) Set the balance to exactly <u>zero</u>. Then <u>add</u> your substance and <u>read off</u> the <u>mass</u>.

3) If you want to transfer the substance to a new container, you need to make sure that the mass you <u>transfer</u> is the <u>same</u> as the mass you <u>measured</u>. There are different ways you can do this. For example:

> • If you're <u>dissolving</u> a mass of a solid in a solvent to make a <u>solution</u>, you could <u>wash</u> any remaining solid into the new container using the <u>solvent</u>.
>
> • You could set the balance <u>to zero</u> before you put your <u>weighing container</u> on the balance. Then <u>reweigh</u> the weighing container <u>after</u> you've transferred the substance. Use the <u>difference</u> in mass to work out <u>exactly</u> how much substance you've transferred.

There Are Different Ways to Measure Liquids

1) There are a few methods you might use to transfer a volume of liquid:

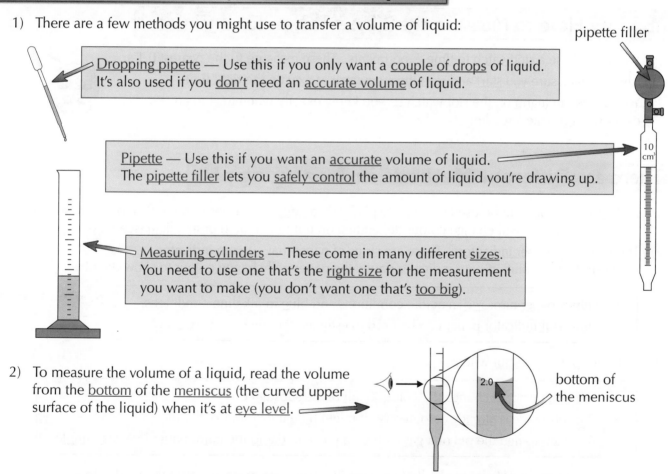

pipette filler

> <u>Dropping pipette</u> — Use this if you only want a <u>couple of drops</u> of liquid. It's also used if you <u>don't</u> need an <u>accurate volume</u> of liquid.

> <u>Pipette</u> — Use this if you want an <u>accurate</u> volume of liquid. The <u>pipette filler</u> lets you <u>safely control</u> the amount of liquid you're drawing up.

10 cm³

> <u>Measuring cylinders</u> — These come in many different <u>sizes</u>. You need to use one that's the <u>right size</u> for the measurement you want to make (you don't want one that's <u>too big</u>).

2) To measure the volume of a liquid, read the volume from the <u>bottom</u> of the <u>meniscus</u> (the curved upper surface of the liquid) when it's at <u>eye level</u>.

2.0

bottom of the meniscus

Remember — always measure liquids at eye level

Measuring substances may not be the most exciting part of doing experiments, but it's really important to remember all the steps and learn how to do it properly. The best kind of revision for these practical techniques is real <u>hands-on experience</u>.

Taking Measurements

You Can **Measure Gas Volumes**

Here are a couple of ways you can measure the volume of a gas:

1) <u>Gas syringe</u> — this is the <u>most accurate</u> way to measure gas volume.

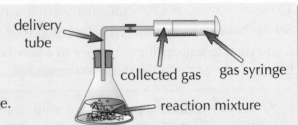

- Make sure the gas syringe is the <u>right size</u> for your measurements.
- Make sure the plunger moves <u>smoothly</u>.
- Read the volume from the <u>scale</u> on the syringe.

delivery tube

collected gas

gas syringe

reaction mixture

2) <u>Upturned measuring cylinder</u> filled with <u>water</u> — read more about this on page 151.

- This method is <u>less accurate</u>.
- But it will give you <u>results</u> that you can <u>compare</u>.

Always make sure your equipment is <u>sealed</u> so no gas can escape. This will make your results more <u>accurate</u>.

You May Have to Measure the **Time Taken** for a Change

stopwatch

1) You should use a <u>stopwatch</u> to <u>time</u> experiments. These measure to the nearest <u>0.1 s</u>.
2) Always make sure you <u>start</u> and <u>stop</u> the stopwatch at exactly the right time.
3) You can set an <u>alarm</u> on the stopwatch so you know exactly when to stop an experiment or take a reading.

There are **Different Methods** for **Measuring pH**

1) <u>Indicator solutions</u> can be used to estimate pH. Add a <u>couple of drops</u> of the indicator to the solution you want to test. It will <u>change colour</u> depending on if it's in an <u>acid</u> or an <u>alkali</u> (see p.76).
2) There are also <u>paper indicators</u>. These are <u>strips of paper</u> that contain indicator. If you <u>spot</u> some solution onto indicator paper, the paper will <u>change colour</u> to show the pH.

- <u>Litmus paper</u> turns <u>red</u> in acidic conditions and <u>blue</u> in alkaline conditions.
- <u>Universal indicator paper</u> can be used to <u>estimate</u> the pH based on its colour.

litmus paper

3) Indicator paper is <u>useful</u> when:

- You <u>don't</u> want to change the colour of <u>all</u> of the substance.
- The substance is <u>already</u> coloured (so it might <u>hide</u> the colour of the indicator).
- You want to find the pH of a <u>gas</u> — hold a piece of <u>damp indicator paper</u> in a <u>gas sample</u>.

4) <u>pH probes</u> measure pH <u>electronically</u> (see page 76). They are more <u>accurate</u> than indicators.

WORKING SCIENTIFICALLY

Have your stopwatch ready before you try to time something

Make sure you learn all the tips on these two pages for improving the accuracy of your measurements — e.g. using the right size of gas syringe for the measurement you're taking.

Safety and Heating Substances

Safety is really important when doing experiments. Read on to find out how to be safe in the lab.

Make Sure You're Working Safely in the Lab

1) Wear sensible clothing (e.g. shoes that will protect your feet from spillages). Also:

   - Wear a lab coat to protect your skin and clothing.
   - Wear safety goggles to protect your eyes, and gloves to protect your hands.

2) Be aware of general safety in the lab. E.g. don't touch any hot equipment.

3) Follow any instructions that your teacher gives you carefully.

4) Chemicals and equipment can be hazardous (dangerous). E.g. some chemicals are flammable (they catch fire easily) — this means you must be careful not to use a Bunsen burner near them.

5) Here are some tips for working with chemicals and equipment safely:

Working with chemicals

1) Make sure you're working in an area that's well ventilated (has a good flow of air).

2) If you're doing an experiment that produces nasty gases (such as chlorine), carry out the experiment in a fume hood. This means the gas can't escape out into the room you're working in.

3) Never touch any chemicals (even if you're wearing gloves):
   - Use a spatula to transfer solids between containers.
   - Carefully pour liquids between containers using a funnel. This will help prevent spillages.

4) Be careful when you're mixing chemicals, as a reaction might occur. E.g. if you're diluting a liquid, always add the concentrated substance to the water. This stops it getting hot.

Working with equipment

1) Use clamp stands to stop equipment falling.

2) Let hot materials cool before moving them. Or wear insulated gloves while handling them.

Water Baths Have Set Temperatures

1) A water bath is a container filled with water. It can be heated to a specific temperature.

2) A simple water bath can be made by heating a beaker of water over a Bunsen burner.

   - The temperature is checked with a thermometer.
   - However, it's hard to keep the temperature of the water constant.

3) An electric water bath will check and change the temperature for you. Here's how you use one:

   - Set the temperature on the water bath.
   - Allow the water to heat up.
   - Place your container (with your substance in it) in the water bath using tongs.
   - The level of the water outside the container should be just above the level of the substance inside it.
   - The substance will be warmed to the same temperature as the water.

A water bath — reaction container — temperature control

The substance in the container is surrounded by water, so the heating is very even.

Heating Substances

Electric Heaters Can Heat Things to High Temperatures

Electric heaters often have a metal plate that can be heated to a specific temperature.

1) Place your container on top of the hot plate.
2) You can heat substances to higher temperatures than you can in a water bath (see previous page). (You can't use a water bath to heat something higher than 100 °C.)
3) You have to stir the substance to make sure it's heated evenly.

Bunsen Burners Heat Things Quickly

Here's how to use a Bunsen burner...

1) Connect the Bunsen burner to a gas tap.
   Check that the hole is closed.
2) Place the Bunsen burner on a heat-proof mat.
3) Light a splint and hold it over the Bunsen burner.
4) Now, turn on the gas.
   The Bunsen burner should light with a yellow flame.
5) Open the hole to turn the flame blue.
   The more open the hole, the hotter the flame.

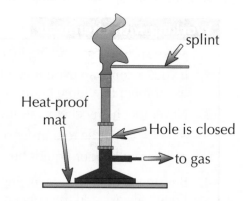

splint

Heat-proof mat

Hole is closed

to gas

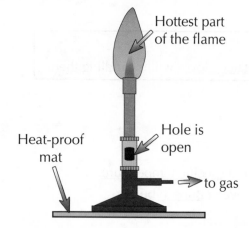

Hottest part of the flame

Heat-proof mat

Hole is open

to gas

6) Heat things just above the blue cone — this is the hottest part of the flame.
7) When the Bunsen burner isn't heating anything, close the hole. This makes the flame yellow and easy to see.
8) If you're heating a container (with your substance in it) in the flame, hold it at the top with a pair of tongs.
9) If you're heating a container over the flame, put a tripod and gauze over the Bunsen burner before you light it. Then place the container on the gauze.

Measure Temperature Using a Thermometer

bulb   thermometer

1) Make sure the bulb of your thermometer is completely under the surface of the substance.
2) If you're taking a starting temperature, you should wait for the temperature to stop changing.
3) Read your measurement off the scale at eye level.

PRACTICAL TIP

You might not expect the blue flame to be hotter, but it is

Always read through any safety precautions you're given carefully before you start a practical.

Setting Up Equipment

Setting up the equipment for an experiment correctly is <u>important</u> if you want to take accurate measurements.

You Can **Collect** a **Gas** in a **Measuring Cylinder**

1) You can use a <u>measuring cylinder</u> turned <u>upside down</u> and filled with <u>water</u> to <u>collect gas</u>.

2) Then you can <u>measure</u> the <u>gas volume</u>. Here's how you do it:

1) <u>Set up</u> the <u>equipment</u> like in the <u>diagram</u>.

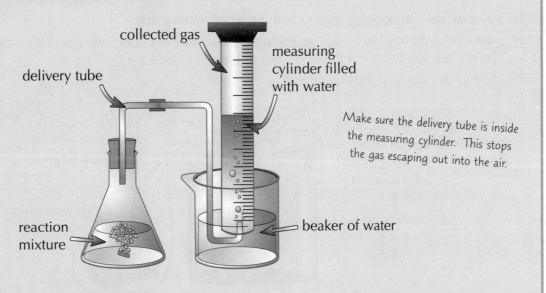

collected gas

delivery tube

measuring cylinder filled with water

Make sure the delivery tube is inside the measuring cylinder. This stops the gas escaping out into the air.

reaction mixture

beaker of water

2) Record the <u>starting level</u> of the water in the measuring cylinder.

3) Any gas from the reaction will pass <u>through</u> the delivery tube and <u>into</u> the <u>measuring cylinder</u>.

4) The gas will <u>push the water out</u> of the measuring cylinder.

5) Record the <u>end level</u> of water in the measuring cylinder.

6) Calculate the <u>volume</u> of gas produced — <u>subtract</u> the <u>end level</u> of water from the <u>starting level</u> of water.

3) You can use the method above to collect a <u>gas sample</u> to <u>test</u>.

- Use a <u>test tube</u> instead of a measuring cylinder.
- When the test tube is full of gas, you can <u>put a bung in it</u>. This lets you <u>store</u> the gas for later.

You can also collect a sample of gas using a gas syringe. There's more on this on page 148.

EXAM TIP

You can test the gas you've collected to find out what it is

Having a <u>good knowledge</u> of practical techniques won't just make your investigations more reliable, it might <u>come in handy</u> for questions in your exams. It's possible that you could be asked to comment on how equipment has been set up, e.g. suggest improvements.

Setting Up Equipment

Some experiments involve slightly more <u>complicated</u> equipment that you might be less familiar with. For example, <u>electrolysis</u> experiments use <u>electrodes</u> — this page shows you how to set them up.

You Can **Identify** the **Products** of Electrolysis

1) When you <u>electrolyse</u> a <u>salt solution</u>:

   There's more about electrolysis on p.82-85.

   - At the <u>cathode</u>, you'll get a <u>pure metal</u> coating the electrode OR bubbles of <u>hydrogen gas</u>.
   - At the <u>anode</u>, you'll get bubbles of <u>oxygen gas</u> OR a <u>halogen</u>.

2) You may have to <u>do some tests</u> to find out what's been <u>made</u>.

3) To do this, you need to <u>set up the equipment</u> correctly to <u>collect</u> any <u>gas</u> that's produced. The easiest way to collect the gas is in a <u>test tube</u>.

4) Here's how to set up the equipment...

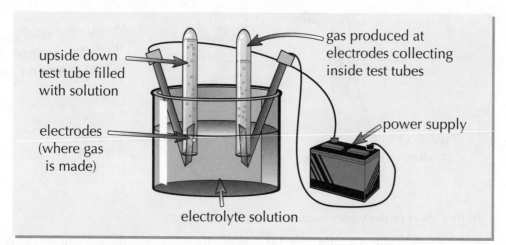

upside down test tube filled with solution

gas produced at electrodes collecting inside test tubes

electrodes (where gas is made)

power supply

electrolyte solution

The tests for gases are described on page 121.

Make Sure You Can **Draw Diagrams** of Your Equipment

1) Your <u>method</u> should include a <u>labelled diagram</u> of how your equipment will be <u>set up</u>.

2) Use <u>scientific drawings</u> — each piece of equipment is drawn as if you're looking at it <u>from the side</u>.

3) For example:

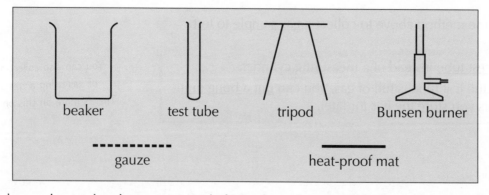

beaker   test tube   tripod   Bunsen burner

gauze   heat-proof mat

4) The <u>beaker</u> and <u>test tube</u> above <u>aren't sealed</u>. To show them <u>sealed</u>, draw a <u>bung</u> in the top.

REVISION TIP

These simple diagrams are clear and easy to draw

Have a go at <u>drawing diagrams</u> of the experimental set-ups on these last few pages. It'll give you some practice at doing them and you can revise how to set up the experiments as well.

Practice Exams

Once you've been through all the questions in this book, you should feel pretty confident about the exams. As final preparation, here is a set of **practice exams** to really get you set for the real thing. The time allowed for each paper is 1 hour 15 minutes. These papers are designed to give you the best possible preparation for your exams.

CGP Practice Exam Paper
GCSE Combined Science

GCSE Combined Science

Chemistry Paper 1

Foundation Tier

In addition to this paper you should have:
- A ruler.
- A calculator.
- The periodic table (page 196).

Centre name				
Centre number				
Candidate number				

Time allowed:
- 1 hour 15 minutes

Surname	
Other names	
Candidate signature	

Instructions to candidates
- Write your name and other details in the spaces provided above.
- Answer **all** questions in the spaces provided.
- Do all rough work on the paper.
- Cross out any work you do not want to be marked.

Information for candidates
- The marks available are given in brackets at the end of each question.
- There are 70 marks available for this paper.
- You are allowed to use a calculator.
- You should use good English and present your answers in a clear and organised way.
- For Question 7.5 ensure that your answer has a clear and logical structure, includes the right scientific terms, spelt correctly, and includes detailed, relevant information.

Advice to candidates
- In calculations show clearly how you worked out your answers.

For examiner's use

Q	Attempt Nº			Q	Attempt Nº		
	1	2	3		1	2	3
1				5			
2				6			
3				7			
4							
			Total				

1 This question is about bonding and elements in the periodic table.

1.1 Which element has 8 electrons in its outer shell?
Tick **one** box.

☐ Oxygen

☐ Lithium

☐ Neon

☐ Nitrogen

[1 mark]

Figure 1 shows a type of bonding.

Figure 1

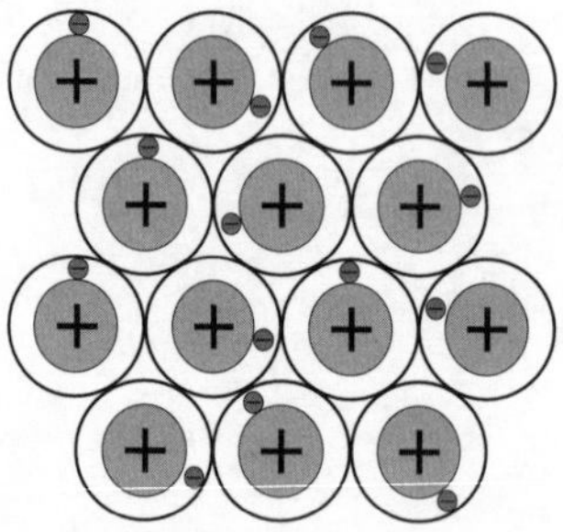

1.2 What type of bonding is shown in **Figure 1**?
Tick **one** box.

☐ Ionic bonding

☐ Intermolecular bonding

☐ Metallic bonding

☐ Covalent bonding

[1 mark]

1.3 Which element has a structure that is held together
by the type of bonding shown in **Figure 1**?
Tick **one** box.

☐ Copper

☐ Helium

☐ Chlorine

☐ Carbon

[1 mark]

The elements in Group 7 of the periodic table are known as the halogens.

1.4 Which of the halogens has the lowest boiling point?
Tick **one** box.

☐ Chlorine

☐ Fluorine

☐ Bromine

☐ Iodine

[1 mark]

1.5 The nuclear symbol for an atom of fluorine is shown below.

$$^{19}_{9}\text{F}$$

How many protons, neutrons and electrons are there in this atom of fluorine?

Protons = ...

Neutrons = ...

Electrons = ...
[3 marks]

The equation for the reaction of chlorine with potassium bromide is:

$$Cl_2 + 2KBr \rightarrow Br_2 + 2KCl$$

1.6 Name the **compound** formed in this reaction.

....
[1 mark]

1.7 Explain why the reactivity of the halogens decreases moving down Group 7.

....

....

....
[2 marks]

Turn over for next question

Turn over ▶

2 Calcium can form the compound calcium carbonate ($CaCO_3$).

The equation for the thermal decomposition of calcium carbonate is:

$$CaCO_3 \rightarrow CaO + CO_2$$

calcium carbonate → calcium oxide + carbon dioxide

2.1 When 2560 g of calcium carbonate decomposed, 1130 g of carbon dioxide was formed. Calculate the mass of calcium oxide formed. Give your answer in standard form.

mass of calcium oxide = ... g

[2 marks]

Solid calcium carbonate also reacts with nitric acid:

$$CaCO_{3(s)} + 2HNO_{3(aq)} \rightarrow Ca(NO_3)_{2(aq)} + H_2O_{(l)} + CO_{2(g)}$$

calcium carbonate + nitric acid → calcium nitrate + water + carbon dioxide

2.2 What do the symbols (aq) and (s) stand for in the equation above?

(aq): ....

(s): ....
[2 marks]

A scientist carries out the reaction between calcium carbonate and nitric acid in a beaker placed on a mass balance.

2.3 Explain why the reading on the mass balance decreases during the reaction.

....

....
[2 marks]

The reaction produces 3.4 g of calcium nitrate.
The volume of the solution at the end of the reaction is 224 cm³.

2.4 Calculate the concentration of calcium nitrate in g/dm³.
Give your answer to 3 significant figures.

concentration of $Ca(NO_3)_2$ = ... g/dm³

[3 marks]

3   A student is using fractional distillation to separate
     a mixture of water, methanol and ethanoic acid.

3.1 What is the meaning of the term 'mixture'?

     ....

     ....
                                                                                        [1 mark]

3.2 Why is fractional distillation described as a physical method of separating substances?

     ☐ No chemical reactions take place during fractional distillation.

     ☐ The student needs to move the apparatus during the distillation.

     ☐ Chemical bonds are broken in fractional distillation.

     ☐ Fractional distillation involves heating.
                                                                                        [1 mark]

The apparatus the student is using is shown in **Figure 2**.

Figure 2

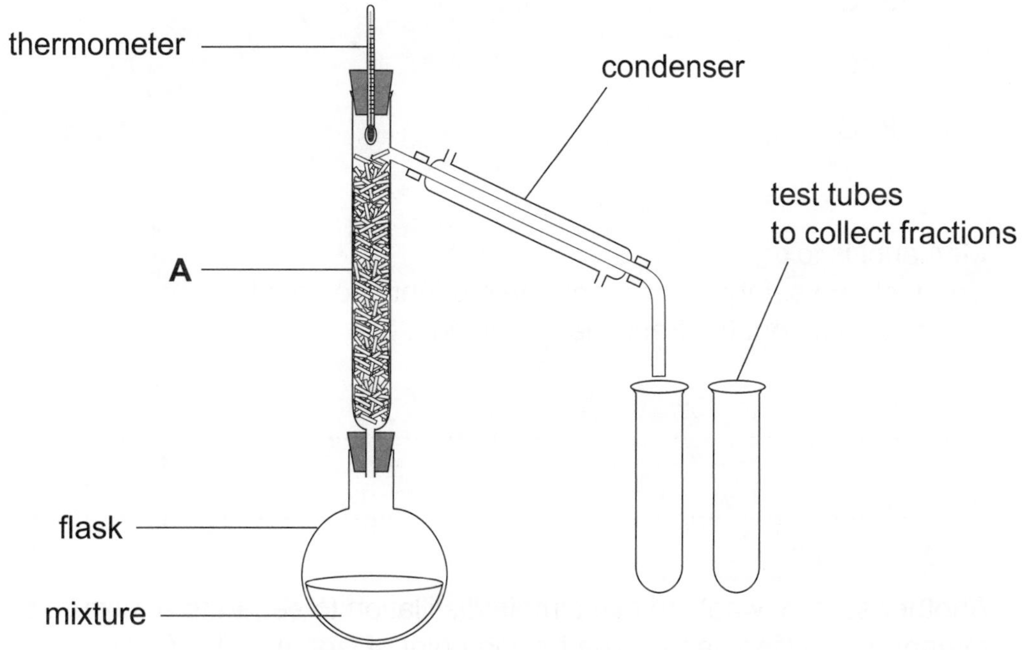

3.3 Name the piece of apparatus labelled **A** in **Figure 2**.

     ....
                                                                                        [1 mark]

Question 3 continues on the next page

Turn over ▶

Table 1 shows the boiling points of the compounds in the student's mixture.

Table 1

Compound	Boiling point in °C
Water	100
Methanol	65
Ethanoic acid	118

3.4 The student plans to collect the first two fractions in test tubes.
Which compound will be left in the **flask** at the end of the distillation?
Give a reason for your answer.

Compound: ....

Reason: ....
[2 marks]

3.5 The student wants to collect a pure sample of methanol.
Which temperature should she heat the mixture to?
Tick **one** box.

☐ 30 °C

☐ 43 °C

☐ 58 °C

☐ 78 °C

[1 mark]

3.6 Methanol is toxic.
Suggest **two** safety precautions the student should take
when carrying out the fractional distillation.

1. ....

2. ....
[2 marks]

Another student wants to use simple distillation to separate a mixture of
methanol and isobutanal. The boiling point of isobutanal is 63 °C.

3.7 Why is simple distillation **not** suitable for separating a mixture of
methanol and isobutanal?

....

....
[1 mark]

4   **Table 2** shows the volume of gas produced in 60 seconds
when four different metals reacted with dilute sulfuric acid.
The metal was the only variable that changed.

Table 2

Metal	Volume of gas produced in cm³
Sodium	97
Calcium	81
Magnesium	62
Zinc	28

4.1   Draw a bar chart on the grid in **Figure 3** using all of the data from **Table 2**.

Figure 3

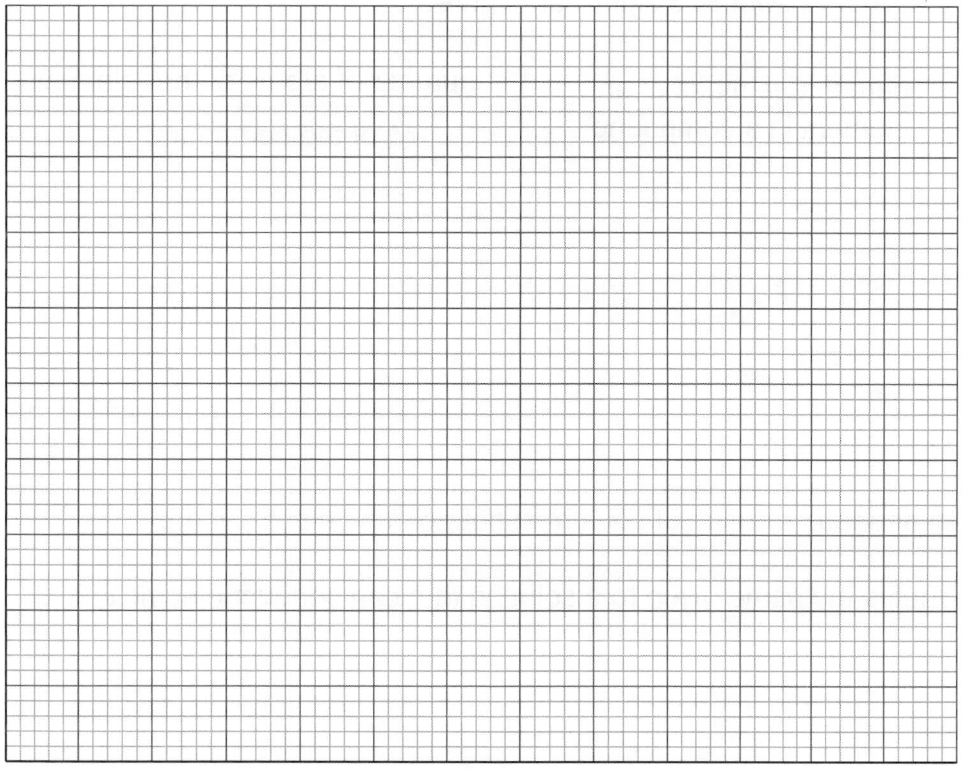

Volume of gas produced in cm³

Metal

[2 marks]

4.2   Name the gas produced during the reactions.

....
[1 mark]

4.3   Use **Table 2** to predict the volume of gas that would be produced in the reaction
between sulfuric acid and iron, if all other variables were kept the same.

volume of gas = ... cm³
[1 mark]

Question 4 continues on the next page

Turn over ▶

One of the products of the reaction of sodium with dilute sulfuric acid
is sodium sulfate, Na_2SO_4.

4.4 Calculate the relative formula mass (M_r) of sodium sulfate.
Relative atomic masses (A_r): O = 16, Na = 23, S = 32

M_r of sodium sulfate = ...

[1 mark]

4.5 Use the equation below to calculate the percentage mass of sodium in sodium sulfate.
Give your answer to 3 significant figures.

$$\text{percentage mass of an element in a compound} = \frac{A_r \times \text{number of atoms of that element}}{M_r \text{ of the compound}} \times 100$$

percentage mass of sodium = ... %

[2 marks]

An aqueous solution of sodium sulfate can be electrolysed.

4.6 What is the name given to a solution that can conduct electricity?

....

[1 mark]

4.7 What is formed at the anode when an aqueous solution of sodium sulfate is electrolysed?

....

[1 mark]

4.8 Name the product formed at the cathode when
an aqueous solution of sodium sulfate is electrolysed.
Give a reason for your answer.

Product at cathode: ....

Reason: ....

....

[2 marks]

5   The elements in Group 1 of the periodic table are known as the alkali metals.
          The first three Group 1 metals are lithium, sodium, and potassium.

5.1   Group 1 metals can react with non-metals to form ionic compounds.
          What is the charge on a Group 1 ion in an ionic compound?
          Tick **one** box.

          ☐ +2

          ☐ +3

          ☐ −1

          ☐ +1

                                                                          [1 mark]

A student watched his teacher carefully place small pieces of lithium, sodium and potassium into cold water. His observations are recorded in **Table 3**.

Table 3

Metal	Observations
lithium	Fizzes, moves across surface.
sodium	Fizzes strongly, moves quickly across surface, appears to melt.
potassium	Fizzes violently, moves very quickly across surface, appears to melt and a flame is seen.

He decides that the order of reactivity of the three metals is:

- potassium (most reactive)

- sodium

- lithium (least reactive)

5.2   Give **two** pieces of evidence from **Table 3** that support the student's conclusion.

1. ....

   ....

2. ....

   ....
                                                                          [2 marks]

Question 5 continues on the next page

Turn over ▶

5.3 Explain the pattern of reactivity that the student has noticed.
Give your answer in terms of the outer electrons of the atoms.

....

....

....

....

[3 marks]

5.4 Which of the following is correct balanced equation
for the reaction between potassium and water?
Tick **one** box.

☐ $2K + H_2O \rightarrow 2KOH + H_2$

☐ $2K + H_2O \rightarrow K_2O + H_2$

☐ $2K + 2H_2O \rightarrow 2KOH + H_2$

☐ $2K + H_2O \rightarrow 2KOH + O_2$

[1 mark]

5.5 Choose the statement that explains why the solution produced
when potassium reacts with water is alkaline.
Tick **one** box.

☐ It contains potassium ions.

☐ It contains water.

☐ It contains an ionic compound.

☐ It contains hydroxide ions.

[1 mark]

5.6 What is the electronic structure of lithium?

....

[1 mark]

6   **Figure 4** shows the apparatus used by a student to measure the temperature change of a reaction between a piece of magnesium and dilute hydrochloric acid.

Figure 4

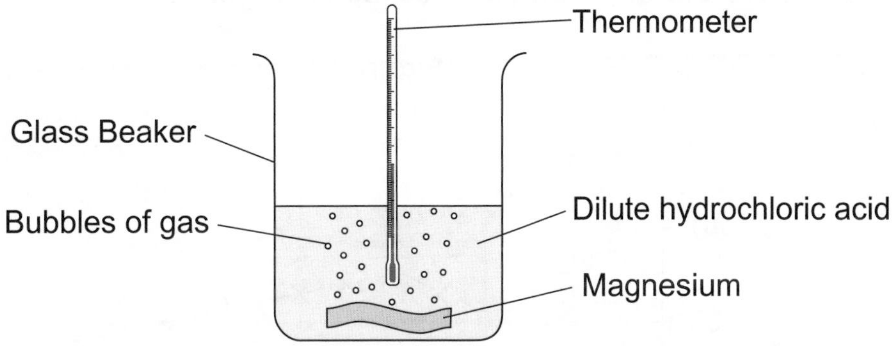

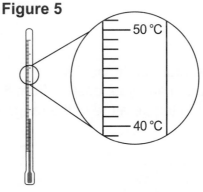

Thermometer

Glass Beaker

Bubbles of gas

Dilute hydrochloric acid

Magnesium

6.1   Suggest **two** changes that the student could make to the apparatus in order to reduce heat loss from her experiment.

1. ....

....

2. ....

....

[2 marks]

6.2   What is the dependent variable in the student's experiment?

....

[1 mark]

6.3   A close up of the thermometer used during the experiment is shown in **Figure 5**.

Figure 5

50 °C

40 °C

What value does each **small division** on the scale of the thermometer represent?
Tick **one** box.

☐   0.1 °C

☐   10 °C

☐   1 °C

☐   2 °C

[1 mark]

Question 6 continues on the next page

Turn over ▶

The student recorded the initial temperature of the dilute hydrochloric acid.
She added the magnesium to the acid.
She then measured the temperature of the reaction mixture every 10 seconds.
The student's results are shown on the graph in **Figure 6**.

Figure 6

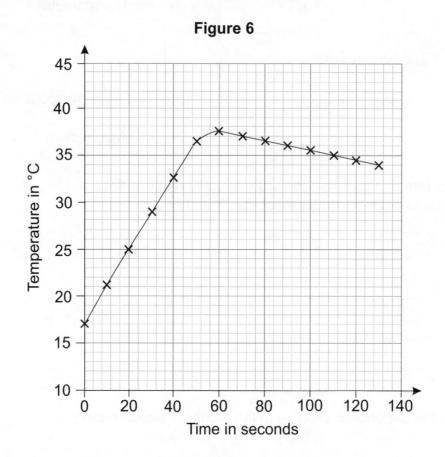

6.4 Using the graph in **Figure 6**, give the highest temperature
of the mixture that the student recorded.

Highest temperature = ... °C

[1 mark]

6.5 The initial temperature of the acid was 17 °C.
Use this information and your answer from **6.4** to estimate
the total change in temperature of the reaction mixture.

....

Temperature change = ... °C

[2 marks]

6.6 State whether this reaction was exothermic or endothermic. Explain your answer.

....

....

[1 mark]

7   The structure and bonding of elements and compounds affects their properties.

7.1   Sodium and chlorine can react together to form an ionic compound.
Figure 7, below, is a dot and cross diagram showing this reaction.

Complete the right-hand side of **Figure 7** by adding the charges of **both** ions
and adding the electrons to the outer shell of the **chloride** ion.

Figure 7

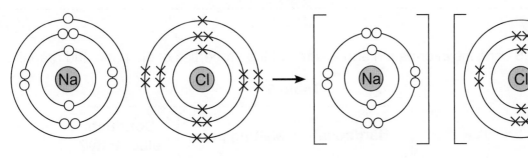

[2 marks]

Table 4 shows some properties of five substances, **A-E**.

Table 4

Substance	Melting point in °C	Boiling point in °C	Does it conduct electricity when solid?	Does it conduct electricity when dissolved or molten?
A	−210	−196	No	No
B	−219	−183	No	No
C	801	1413	No	Yes
D	115	445	No	No
E	1083	2567	Yes	Yes

7.2   At which temperature would substance **B** be a gas?
Tick **one** box.

☐ −207 °C

☐ −184 °C

☐ 63 °C

☐ −220 °C

[1 mark]

7.3   Substance **A** is made up of small, covalently bonded molecules.
Explain why substance **A** has a relatively low melting point.

....

....

[2 marks]

Question 7 continues on the next page

Turn over ▶

7.4 Look at **Table 4**. One of the substances, **A-E**, is an ionic compound.
Use the information in the table to suggest which of the substances is ionic.
Explain your answer.

....

....

....

[2 marks]

7.5 **Table 5** contains information about some of the properties of diamond and graphite.

Table 5

	Hardness	Melting point	Conducts electricity?
Diamond	Hard	High	No
Graphite	Soft	High	Yes

Explain these properties of diamond and graphite
in terms of their structure and bonding.

....

....

....

....

....

....

....

....

....

....

[6 marks]

END OF QUESTIONS

GCSE Combined Science

Chemistry Paper 2

Foundation Tier

In addition to this paper you should have:
- A ruler.
- A calculator.
- The periodic table (page 196).

Centre name				
Centre number				
Candidate number				

Time allowed:
- 1 hour 45 minutes

Surname	
Other names	
Candidate signature	

Instructions to candidates
- Write your name and other details in the spaces provided above.
- Answer **all** questions in the spaces provided.
- Do all rough work on the paper.
- Cross out any work you do not want to be marked.

Information for candidates
- The marks available are given in brackets at the end of each question.
- There are 70 marks available for this paper.
- You are allowed to use a calculator.
- You should use good English and present your answers in a clear and organised way.
- For Questions 3.4 and 7.3 ensure that your answer has a clear and logical structure, includes the right scientific terms, spelt correctly, and includes detailed, relevant information.

Advice to candidates
- In calculations show clearly how you worked out your answers.

For examiner's use

Q	Attempt Nº			Q	Attempt Nº		
	1	2	3		1	2	3
1				5			
2				6			
3				7			
4							
Total							

1 This question is about resources and crude oil.

1.1 What is the meaning of the term 'finite resource'?
Tick **one** box.

☐ A resource that is natural product.

☐ A resource that is used up more quickly than it can be replaced.

☐ A resource that can be replaced fairly quickly.

☐ A resource that can be burned to produce energy.

[1 mark]

Table 1 shows the time it takes for some different resources to form.

Table 1

Resource	Time it takes to form in years
Resource 1	4000
Resource 2	10^7
Resource 3	1
Resource 4	65 000

1.2 Which of the resources is a renewable resource?
Tick **one** box.

☐ Resource 1

☐ Resource 2

☐ Resource 3

☐ Resource 4

[1 mark]

1.3 **Figure 1** shows a technique used to separate crude oil into groups of hydrocarbons.

Figure 1

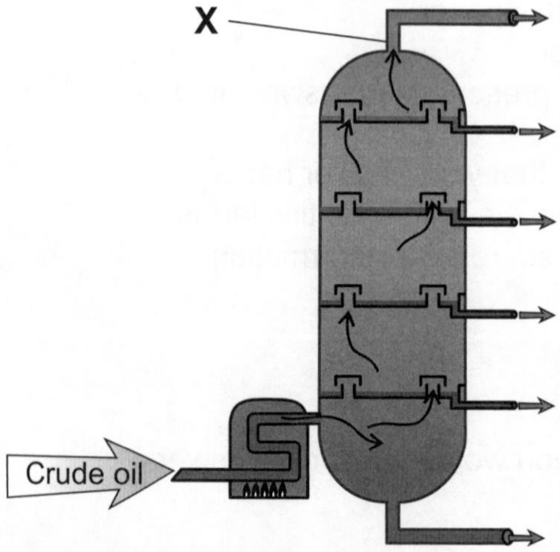

Name the technique shown in **Figure 1**.

....

[1 mark]

1.4 The technique shown in **Figure 1** relies on the properties of the groups of hydrocarbons. Complete the sentences. Use words from the box.

boiling points   decomposes   evaporates   melting points   melts   reactivities

Before it enters the column, the crude oil is heated until it ....

Different hydrocarbons from the crude oil then leave the column at different points

because they have different ....

[2 marks]

1.5 The products listed in **Table 2** are groups of hydrocarbons produced using the technique shown in **Figure 1**.

Table 2

Product	Approximate length of carbon chain
Petrol	8
Kerosene	15
Diesel oil	20
Bitumen	>40

Which of these products will be collected closest to the point marked **X** on **Figure 1**?
Tick **one** box.

☐ Petrol

☐ Kerosene

☐ Diesel oil

☐ Bitumen

[1 mark]

1.6 Which of the products in **Table 2** could be cracked to produce diesel oil?
Tick **one** box.

☐ Petrol

☐ Kerosene

☐ Bitumen

☐ None of them

[1 mark]

1.7 Which type of substance is a product of cracking?
Tick **one** box.

☐ Alkene

☐ Salt

☐ Polymer

☐ Catalyst

[1 mark]

Turn over for next question

2 A student carried out a chromatography experiment to identify an unknown food colouring.

This is the method used:

1. Draw a pencil baseline on a sheet of paper.
   Add a spot of the unknown food colouring to the baseline.

2. Add spots of two reference food colourings, **A** and **B**, to the baseline.

3. Place the sheet of paper in a beaker containing a small amount of solvent.
   Put a lid on the beaker.

4. When the solvent has almost reached the top of the piece of paper,
   remove the paper and leave it to dry.

2.1 What is the purpose of the solvent in this experiment?
Tick **one** box.

☐ It is a reactant

☐ It is the stationary phase

☐ It is a catalyst

☐ It is the mobile phase

[1 mark]

2.2 Only a small amount of solvent is used so that it does not touch the baseline
when the paper is first placed in the beaker.
Why should the solvent not touch the baseline?

....
[1 mark]

2.3 How could the student test the reproducibility of the experiment?

....

....

....
[2 marks]

Figure 2 shows the chromatogram produced during the experiment.

Figure 2

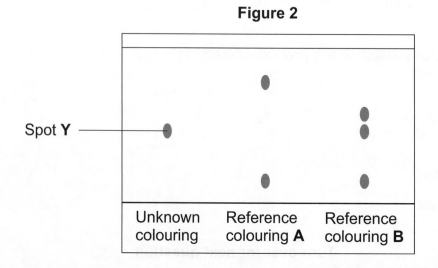

Spot **Y**

2.4 Which of the three food colourings is most likely to be a pure substance? Use **Figure 2** to justify your answer.

....

....

[1 mark]

2.5 What is the minimum number of substances in reference colouring **B**?

....

[1 mark]

2.6 The R_f value for spot **Y** is calculated using the equation:

$$R_f = \frac{\text{distance moved by spot } \mathbf{Y} \text{ from the baseline}}{\text{distance moved by solvent from the baseline}}$$

Calculate the R_f value for spot **Y** on **Figure 2**.
Give your answer to two significant figures.

R_f value =...............................

[5 marks]

In another experiment the student measured the melting point of a sample of a substance found in a different food colouring. **Table 3** shows his result, as well as the data book value for the melting point of the substance.

Table 3

Experimental melting point in °C	133
Data book melting point in °C	142

2.7 Is the student's sample pure? Use the data from **Table 3** to justify your answer.

....

....

....

[1 mark]

Turn over for next question

Turn over ▶

3   **Figure 3** shows how the concentration of carbon dioxide in the atmosphere has changed since 1700.

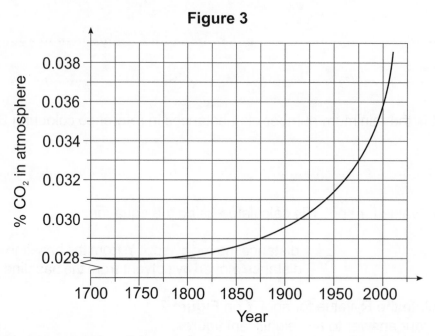

Figure 3

3.1   Use **Figure 3** to describe how the concentration of carbon dioxide in the atmosphere has changed since 1700.

....

....

....

[2 marks]

3.2   Which piece of information would help convince a scientist that the data in **Figure 3** is valid? Tick **one** box.

☐   The data covers a long period of time.

☐   The data has been published in a book.

☐   The percentage of CO_2 has been given to three decimal places.

☐   The data has been peer-reviewed.

[1 mark]

Figure 4 shows a process that takes place in Earth's atmosphere.

Figure 4

3.3 What is the name of the process shown in **Figure 4**?
Tick **one** box.

☐ Air pollution

☐ Greenhouse effect

☐ Thermal radiation

☐ Climate change

[1 mark]

3.4 A drinks company is investigating whether using glass bottles or plastic bottles will have less impact on the environment. They produce some designs for glass and plastic bottles and carry out some research into the manufacturing, transport and recycling processes for each. **Table 4** shows the information they found.

Table 4

	Glass bottle	Plastic bottle
CO_2 given out during production	255 g	193 g
Mass of bottle	402 g	44 g
CO_2 given out transporting by road	39 g	12 g
Recycled content	Contains 83% recycled material.	Contains no recycled material.
Recycling	Can be recycled endlessly. The company estimates 65% of these bottles would be recycled after use.	Can be recycled once or twice. The company estimates 55% of these bottles sold would be recycled after use.

Use the information in **Table 4** and your own knowledge to compare the environmental impacts of using glass bottles and using plastic bottles.

....

....

....

....

....

....

....

....

[4 marks]

Turn over for next question

Turn over ▶

4   A student is investigating how the rate of the reaction between calcium carbonate and sulfuric acid is affected by the concentration of the acid.

The student uses the following method:

- Weigh out 0.7 g of calcium carbonate.
- Add the calcium carbonate to an excess of 7.3 g/dm³ sulfuric acid in a conical flask.
- Use a gas syringe to collect the gas given off by the reaction.
- Measure and record the volume of gas produced every 10 s.
- Repeat the experiment using sulfuric acid with a concentration of 14.6 g/dm³.

4.1   To make each run a fair test, the student keeps the mass of calcium carbonate the same. Suggest **two** other variables that the student should keep the same to make each run a fair test.

1. ....

2. ....

[2 marks]

4.2   The gas produced by the reaction is carbon dioxide.
Which test could be used to confirm that the gas is carbon dioxide?
Tick **one** box.

☐   Holding a lit splint at the open end of a test tube containing the gas.

☐   Putting damp litmus paper into a test tube containing the gas.

☐   Putting a glowing splint inside a test tube containing the gas.

☐   Bubbling the gas through a solution of calcium hydroxide.

[1 mark]

The graph in **Figure 5** shows the student's results for the first experiment, using 7.3 g/dm^3 sulfuric acid, and the second experiment, using 14.6 g/dm^3.

Figure 5

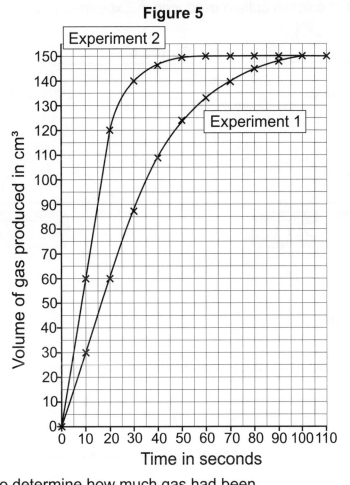

4.3 Use **Figure 5** to determine how much gas had been produced in each experiment after 30 seconds.

Volume of gas produced after 30 seconds in Experiment 1 = ...cm^3

Volume of gas produced after 30 seconds in Experiment 2 = ...cm^3

[2 marks]

4.4 Describe one way in which the shapes of the curves in **Figure 2** show that the rate of reaction was faster in Experiment 2 than in Experiment 1.

....

....

[1 mark]

4.5 In terms of collision theory, explain why concentration affects the rate of a reaction.

....

....

....

....

[2 marks]

Question 4 continues on the next page

Turn over ▶

4.6 The reaction also produces calcium sulfate. **Figure 6** shows how the student used a mass balance and a weighing boat to measure the mass in grams of calcium sulfate produced in Experiment 2.

Figure 6

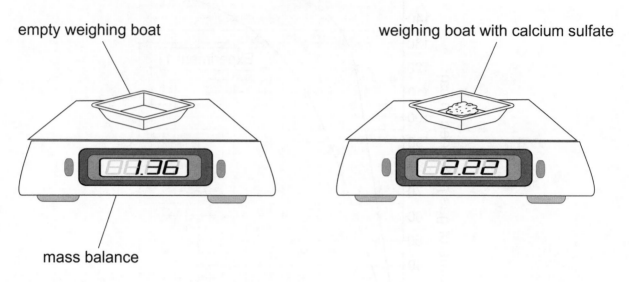

empty weighing boat

weighing boat with calcium sulfate

mass balance

Calculate the mass of calcium sulfate formed in Experiment 2.

mass of calcium sulfate formed = ... g

[1 mark]

4.7 Use **Figure 5** and your answer to question **4.6** to calculate the mean rate of reaction during Experiment 2.
The mean rate of reaction is calculated using the equation:

$$\text{mean rate of reaction} = \frac{\text{amount of product formed}}{\text{time taken}}$$

Give your answer to 2 significant figures.

mean rate of reaction = ... g/s

[3 marks]

5   Alkanes are hydrocarbon compounds found in crude oil. **Table 5** shows
how the boiling points of some alkanes change as the molecules get bigger.

Table 5

Alkane	Molecular formula	Boiling point (°C)
Propane	C_3H_8	−42
Butane	C_4H_{10}	−1
Pentane	C_5H_{12}	
Hexane	C_6H_{14}	69
Heptane	C_7H_{16}	98

5.1   On **Figure 7**:

- plot the boiling points of propane, butane, hexane and heptane against number of carbon atoms,
- draw a smooth curve through the points you have plotted.

Figure 7

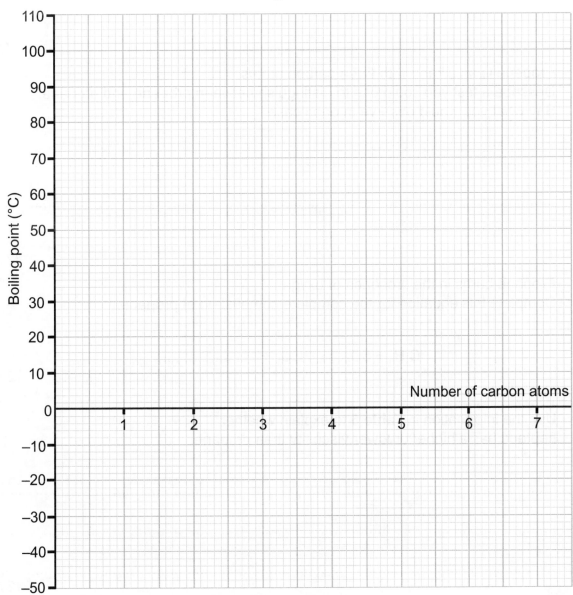

[2 marks]

Question 5 continues on the next page

Turn over ▶

5.2 Use your graph to estimate the boiling point of pentane.

.... °C

[1 mark]

5.3 What is the general formula of the alkanes? Tick **one** box.

☐ C_nH_{2n}

☐ C_nH_{2n+1}

☐ C_nH_{2n+2}

☐ C_nH_{2n-1}

[1 mark]

5.4 Propane is an alkane with three carbon atoms.
Draw the displayed formula of propane.

[1 mark]

5.5 Propene is an alkene with three carbon atoms.
Describe a test you could use to distinguish between propene and propane.
Say what you would observe in each case.

....

....

....

[3 marks]

5.6 Propane burns in the presence of oxygen.
Complete this equation for the complete combustion of propane.

$$C_3H_8 + 5O_2 \rightarrow 3CO_2 + \ ....$$

[2 marks]

5.7 Use the information in **Table 5** to explain whether
heptane has a higher or lower viscosity than propane.

....

....

....

[2 marks]

6   Nitrogen dioxide is an atmospheric pollutant that irritates the respiratory system.
It is thought that there is a link between exposure to nitrogen dioxide and the
severity of asthma attacks in people with asthma.

Figure 8 shows the results of a study carried out by a group of scientists.
The study compared atmospheric nitrogen dioxide levels with the severity of asthma
attacks suffered by men under the age of 40 working in a city centre. The severity of
asthma attacks were measured on a scale of 1 to 10, with 10 being the most severe.

Figure 8

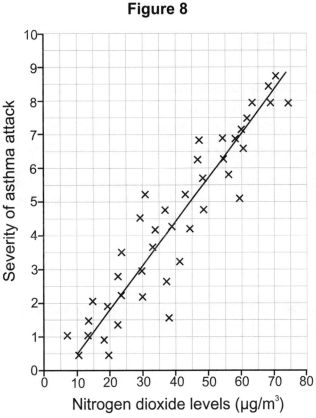

6.1   Describe the relationship between the level of nitrogen dioxide
in the air and the severity of asthma attacks shown in **Figure 8**.

....

....

[1 mark]

6.2   The scientists hope to draw a conclusion about the link between the
nitrogen dioxide level and the severity of asthma attacks.

Suggest why they cannot use the results shown in **Figure 8**
to draw a conclusion that applies to **everyone**.

....

....

[1 mark]

Question 6 continues on the next page

Turn over ▶

6.3   Where do the oxides of nitrogen in the air come from?
Suggest why levels of nitrogen oxides can be particularly high in cities.

....

....

....

....

[3 marks]

6.4   Oxides of nitrogen can cause acid rain.
Acid rain is acidic because it contains nitric acid, HNO_3.
The equation for the reaction of nitric acid with water is:

$$HNO_3 + H_2O \rightleftharpoons H_3O^+ + NO_3^-$$

Heating the reaction mixture causes the reaction to go in the backwards direction.
How can the reaction be made to go in the forwards direction?

....

[1 mark]

6.5   Oxides of nitrogen are not the only gases that can cause acid rain.
Name **one** other pollutant gas that can cause acid rain.

....

[1 mark]

7   In the UK, the majority of our drinking water is produced from treating groundwater or surface water. Drinking water can also be made by treating sea water or waste water.

7.1   Producing water that is safe to drink from sea water is expensive.
Suggest why some countries produce drinking water by this method.

....

[1 mark]

7.2   What is the name of the process used to remove salt from sea water?
Tick **one** box.

☐   Filtration

☐   Desalination

☐   Sterilisation

☐   Cracking

[1 mark]

7.3   A teacher gives a student a sample of sea water,
and asks her to produce a sample of pure water from it.
Plan a method that the student could use to remove the salt from the sea water.

....

....

....

....

....

....

....

....

....

....

....

[6 marks]

Question 7 continues on the next page

Turn over ▶

182

7.4 Sewage treatment plants process sewage and release clean, treated water back into the environment. The first step in the treatment of sewage is screening.
What happens in the screening step?
Tick **one** box.

☐ Chlorine is added to the sewage to kill microorganisms.

☐ The sewage is placed into large storage tanks and allowed to settle.

☐ Anaerobic digestion is used to break down the sewage.

☐ Large bits of material (such as grit) are removed from the sewage.

[1 mark]

7.5 Following screening, sedimentation is used to separate the effluent from the sludge. Describe what happens to the effluent before it can be returned to the environment.

....

....

....
[2 marks]

END OF QUESTIONS

Topic 1 — Atomic Structure and the Periodic Table

Pages 23-24
Warm-Up Questions
1) The total number of protons and neutrons.
2) An element is a substance made up of atoms that all have the same number of protons in their nucleus.
3) False
4) calcium chloride
5) $2K + 2H_2O \rightarrow 2KOH + H_2$

Exam Questions
1.1

Relative charge of a proton	Relative charge of a neutron
+1	0

[1 mark]

1.2 in the nucleus *[1 mark]*
1.3 8 *[1 mark]*
Atoms have the same number of protons as electrons. This is what makes them neutral.
1.4 1 *[1 mark]*
2.1 12 *[1 mark]*
2.2 11 *[1 mark]*
2.3 Na *[1 mark]*
3.1 methane and oxygen *[1 mark]*
3.2 carbon dioxide and water *[1 mark]*
3.3 oxygen/O_2 *[1 mark]*
3.4 $CH_4 + 2O_2 \rightarrow CO_2 + 2H_2O$ *[1 mark]*
4.1 **$H_2SO_4 + 2NH_3 \rightarrow (NH_4)_2SO_4$** *[1 mark for correct reactants, 1 mark for correctly balancing the equation]*
4.2 4 *[1 mark]*
These elements are hydrogen, sulfur, oxygen and nitrogen.
4.3 8 *[1 mark]*
There are 4 hydrogen atoms in NH_4 and there are two lots of NH_4 present in the formula of ammonium sulfate.
5.1 Isotopes are different forms of the same element, which have the same number of **protons** *[1 mark]* but different numbers of **neutrons** *[1 mark]*.
5.2 5 *[1 mark]*
The number of protons in an atom is equal to its atomic number.
5.3 $(20 \times 10) + (80 \times 11) = 1080$
Relative atomic mass $= 1080 \div 100 = \textbf{10.8}$
[3 marks for correct answer, otherwise 1 mark for calculating sum of (isotope abundance × isotope mass number), 1 mark for dividing by 100.]

Page 31
Warm-Up Questions
1) False
2) evaporation / crystallisation
3) the top

Exam Questions
1.1 Put the paper in a beaker of solvent *[1 mark]*.
1.2 Pencil marks are insoluble/won't dissolve in the solvent / pen would dissolve in the solvent *[1 mark]*.
2 Step 1 is to dissolve the ammonium sulfate *[1 mark]*.
Step 2 is to remove the sharp sand *[1 mark]*.
Step 3 is to evaporate the water and produce dry crystals of ammonium sulfate *[1 mark]*.

3.1 How to grade your answer:
Level 0: There is no relevant information. *[No marks]*
Level 1: Some steps of the method and some relevant safety precautions are included, but the answer is not in a logical order. Following the method given would not produce the results desired. *[1 to 2 marks]*
Level 2: Most of the method and safety precautions are described, but the steps may not be in a completely logical order and some detail may be missing. *[3 to 4 marks]*
Level 3: The method and safety precautions are described in full, with the steps given in a logical order. Following the method would produce the results desired. *[5 to 6 marks]*
Here are some points your answer may include:
Method
Put the solution of propanone and water in the flask and heat it.
Monitor the temperature using the thermometer.
Heat the mixture until the temperature reaches around 56 °C.
56 °C is the boiling point of propanone, so at this temperature the propanone in the solution will start to evaporate and turn into a gas.
The boiling point of water is higher (100 °C), so at 56 °C the water will remain as a liquid.
The propanone gas travels from the flask into the condenser.
In the condenser, the gas is cooled and condenses/turns back into a liquid.
The liquid propanone runs out of the condenser and is collected in the beaker.
The water is left behind in the flask.
Safety precautions
Take care with Bunsen burner/heat source.
Alternatively, use a heat source that doesn't involve a flame, such as a water bath or electric heater.
Avoid touching hot glassware.
Make sure no solution gets on the outside of the flask where it could catch fire.
Make sure the flask is tightly sealed so no propanone gas escapes.
Work in a fume cupboard.
Wear a lab coat, gloves and goggles.
3.2 fractional distillation *[1 mark]*
The boiling points of water and methanoic acid are too close together to allow them to be separated by simple distillation, so fractional distillation must be used.

Page 37
Warm-Up Questions
1) In the 'plum pudding' model, the atom is a ball of positive charge, with negatively charged electrons scattered in this ball.
2) a) 2
b) 8
3) Mendeleev left gaps in his table so that elements with similar properties stayed in the same groups.

Exam Questions

1.1   by atomic mass *[1 mark]*

1.2   by atomic number *[1 mark]*

1.3   They have the same number of electrons in their outer shell *[1 mark]*.

2.1

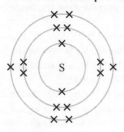

[1 mark]

It's fine if you used dots instead of crosses to show the electrons in your diagram.

2.2   Group 6 *[1 mark]*

2.3   Any one from: oxygen / selenium / tellurium / polonium / livermorium *[1 mark]*

2.4   2 *[1 mark]*

Pages 44-45

Warm-Up Questions

1)   positive ions

2)   Any two from: e.g. strong / can be bent or hammered into different shapes (malleable) / conduct heat / conduct electricity / high melting point / high boiling point.

3)   lithium chloride / LiCl

4)   negative

5)   Group 0

Exam Questions

1.1   fluorine *[1 mark]*.

1.2   iodine *[1 mark]*

2.1   alkali metals *[1 mark]*

2.2   To the right of the line *[1 mark]*. Since it does not conduct electricity, it must be a non-metal *[1 mark]*.

3.1   They have a single outer electron which is easily lost so they are very reactive *[1 mark]*.

3.2   potassium hydroxide *[1 mark]* and hydrogen *[1 mark]*

3.3   The outer electron is further from the nucleus and so less attracted to the nucleus *[1 mark]*.

4.1   ionic bonds *[1 mark]*

4.2   displacement reaction *[1 mark]*

4.3   Chlorine is more reactive than iodine *[1 mark]*, because more reactive elements displace less reactive elements in displacement reactions / chlorine displaces iodine from the potassium iodide *[1 mark]*.

4.4   Group 0 elements don't need to lose or gain electrons to have a full outer shell. / Group 0 elements already have a full outer shell *[1 mark]*.

Topic 2 — Bonding, Structure and Properties of Matter

Page 52

Warm-Up Questions

1)   A charged particle

2)   1–

3)   high

4)   True

5) $Al(OH)_3$

Exam Questions

1.1

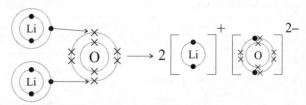

[1 mark for correct electron arrangement and charge on lithium ion, 1 mark for correct electron arrangement and charge on oxygen ion]

1.2   LiCl *[1 mark]*

2.1   Sodium ions have a 1+ charge and chloride ions have a 1– charge *[1 mark]* so one sodium ion is needed to balance the charge on one chloride ion *[1 mark]* (so the empirical formula is NaCl).

2.2   Sodium chloride contains many strong ionic bonds *[1 mark]* which require a lot of energy to break *[1 mark]*.

2.3   In solid sodium chloride, the ions are held in place, so cannot conduct electricity *[1 mark]*. In molten sodium chloride, the ions are free to move, so can conduct electricity *[1 mark]*.

2.4   Dissolve it in water/solution *[1 mark]*.

Page 56

Warm-Up Questions

1)   A chemical bond made by the sharing of a pair of electrons between two atoms.

2)   1

3)   False

Most simple molecular substances are gases or liquids at room temperature.

4)   covalent bonds

Exam Questions

1.1   8 *[1 mark]*

1.2   3 *[1 mark]*

1.3   0 *[1 mark]*

All the bonds in the molecule are single covalent bonds — you get double bonds in molecules like oxygen.

2

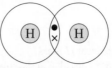

[1 mark for showing 1 pair of shared electrons between H atoms]

3.1   1 *[1 mark]*

3.2   The forces of attraction between molecules/intermolecular forces are very weak, so are easily overcome *[1 mark]*.

3.3   Hydrogen chloride isn't charged / doesn't contain any ions or delocalised electrons to carry a charge *[1 mark]*.

Page 61
Warm-Up Questions
1) True
2) solid
3) E.g. diamond is much harder than graphite. Diamond doesn't conduct electricity whereas graphite does.
4) The layers of atoms/ions in metals are able to slide over each other.

Exam Questions
1

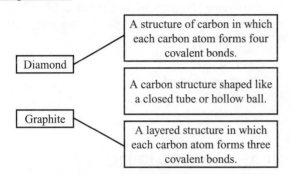

| Diamond | A structure of carbon in which each carbon atom forms four covalent bonds. |

A carbon structure shaped like a closed tube or hollow ball.

| Graphite | A layered structure in which each carbon atom forms three covalent bonds. |

[1 mark for each correctly drawn line]

2.1 In a giant covalent structure, all of the atoms are bonded to each other with strong covalent bonds *[1 mark]*. It takes lots of energy to break these bonds and melt the solid *[1 mark]*.
2.2 E.g. diamond / graphite / silicon dioxide *[1 mark]*
3.1 A metal mixed with another metal (or element) *[1 mark]*.
3.2 The delocalised electrons are free to move *[1 mark]*, so can carry thermal/heat energy *[1 mark]*.
3.3 Iron is a metal, so has a regular arrangement of atoms *[1 mark]*, which means that they can slide over each other *[1 mark]*, making iron soft. Steel contains different sized atoms *[1 mark]* which makes it harder for them to slide over each other *[1 mark]* (which makes it hard).

Page 65
Warm-Up Questions
1) Solid
2) True
3) The forces of attraction increase and lots of bonds form between the gas particles, so the gas becomes a liquid.
4) $Na^+_{(aq)}$

Exam Questions
1 In solids, there are **strong** *[1 mark]* forces of attraction between particles, which hold them in fixed positions in a **regular** *[1 mark]* arrangement. The particles don't **move** *[1 mark]* from their positions, so solids keep their shape. The **hotter** *[1 mark]* the solid becomes, the more the particles in the solid vibrate.
2.1 C *[1 mark]*
2.2 Boiling/evaporation *[1 mark]*
2.3 The particles are free to move about / only have weak forces of attraction between them *[1 mark]*, so they spread out to fill the container *[1 mark]*.

Topic 3 — Quantitative Chemistry

Pages 71-72
Warm-Up Questions
1) The sum of the relative atomic masses of all the atoms in a compound.
2) $(2 \times 1) + 16 = 18$
3) True
4) One of the reactants is a gas that is found in air, and all the products are solids, liquids or in solution.
5) g/dm^3

Exam Questions
1 111 *[1 mark]*
M_r of $CaCl_2 = 40 + (35.5 \times 2) = 111$
2 magnesium fluoride, MgF_2 *[1 mark]*
3 $48.6 + 26.4 = 75.0$ kg *[1 mark]*
4 M_r of $Zn(CN)_2 = 65 + ((12 + 14) \times 2) = $ **117** *[1 mark]*
5.1 M_r of $Ca(OH)_2 = 40 + ((16 + 1) \times 2) = $ **74** *[1 mark]*
5.2 Total mass of reactants $= 18.5$ g $+ 31.5$ g $= 50$ g
So mass of calcium nitrate $= 50$ g $- 9$ g $= $ **41 g** *[1 mark]*
6.1 M_r of $MgCO_3 = 24 + 12 + (16 \times 3) = $ **84** *[1 mark]*
6.2 The mass will decrease *[1 mark]*
7.1 $1500 \div 1000 = $ **1.5 dm³**
1000 cm³ $= 1$ dm³
7.2 mass $=$ concentration $\times$ volume $= 12 \times 1.5 = $ **18 g**
[2 marks for correct answer, otherwise 1 mark for correct working.]
8.1 concentration $=$ mass $\div$ volume $= 40 \div 0.25 = $ **160 g/dm³**
[2 marks for correct answer, otherwise 1 mark for correct working.]
8.2 M_r of $KOH = 39 + 16 + 1 = 56$
Percentage mass of potassium in KOH
$= \dfrac{A_r \text{ of potassium} \times \text{number of atoms of potassium}}{M_r \text{ of potassium hydroxide}} \times 100$
$= \dfrac{39 \times 1}{56} \times 100 = 69.642...\% = $ **69.6%**
[3 marks for correct answer rounded to 3 s.f., otherwise 2 marks for correct answer not rounded to 3 s.f., or 1 mark for correct M_r of KOH.]

Topic 4 — Chemical Changes

Page 77
Warm-Up Questions
1) 0-14
2) Neutral
3) False
Universal indicator turns green if it is added to a substance with a pH of 7.
4) $CaCO_3$
5) Copper sulfate and water

Exam Questions
1.1 OH^- *[1 mark]*
1.2 neutralisation *[1 mark]*
2.1 Alkalis *[1 mark]*
2.2 $2HNO_3 + Mg(OH)_2 \rightarrow Mg(NO_3)_2 + 2H_2O$
[1 mark for formulas of both products correct, 1 mark for putting a 2 in front of H_2O to balance the equation]
3.1 Calcium chloride *[1 mark]*
3.2 The salt will be contaminated by the indicator *[1 mark]*.

3.3 How to grade your answer:

Level 0: There is no relevant information. *[No marks]*

Level 1: Simple statements are made relating to relevant scientific techniques, however points are not linked, and the answer lacks detail.
[1 to 2 marks]

Level 2: A coherent answer is given that follows a logical order and shows a good understanding of the relevant scientific techniques, including filtration and crystallisation. However, some detail may be missing. *[3 to 4 marks]*

Level 3: A detailed and coherent description of a relevant scientific technique is given. The answer shows a clear understanding of the techniques of filtration and crystallisation.
[5 to 6 marks]

Here are some points your answer may include:

Gently warm the hydrochloric acid using a Bunsen burner/ water bath, then turn off the Bunsen burner/remove the acid from the water bath.

Add the calcium carbonate to the warmed hydrochloric acid until no more reacts / there is calcium carbonate at the bottom of the flask.

Use filter paper and a funnel to filter the solution, in order to remove any unreacted calcium carbonate.

Crystallise the solution by gently heating it using a water bath/electric heater to evaporate off some of the water.

Then leave the solution to cool.

Crystals of calcium chloride/the soluble salt should form.

The crystals can be filtered out of the solution and then dried.

Page 81
Warm-Up Questions

1) True
2) magnesium chloride
3) A metal hydroxide and hydrogen

Exam Questions

1 Magnesium *[1 mark]*
2.1 potassium/sodium/calcium *[1 mark]*
2.2 copper *[1 mark]*
Metals below hydrogen in the reactivity series don't react with acids.
2.3 The reaction with iron would be less violent than with zinc *[1 mark]* because iron is less reactive/ lower in the reactivity series than zinc *[1 mark]*.
2.4 potassium/sodium/calcium/magnesium *[1 mark]*
Carbon can only be used to extract metals that are below it in the reactivity series. Metals above carbon must be extracted using electrolysis.
3.1 The copper was displaced from its salt *[1 mark]*.
3.2 Zinc is more reactive/higher in the reactivity series than copper *[1 mark]*.
3.3 e.g. iron *[1 mark]*
Metal X must be more reactive than copper (as it displaces copper from copper sulfate), but less reactive than zinc (which it doesn't displace from zinc sulfate).

Page 86
Warm-Up Questions

1) The cathode
2) True
3) Hydrogen gas

Exam Questions

1 When molten sodium chloride is electrolysed, the **negative** *[1 mark]* chloride ions move towards the anode and form chlorine gas. At the cathode, the **sodium** *[1 mark]* ions gain electrons.
The sodium chloride is molten, so there are no hydrogen ions present to compete with the sodium ions at the cathode.
2.1 Pb^{2+} *[1 mark]*
2.2 Br^- *[1 mark]*
2.3 Molten lead *[1 mark]*
2.4 Br_2 *[1 mark]*

Topic 5 — Energy Changes

Page 91
Warm-Up Questions

1) True
2) E.g. in hand warmers/self-heating cans/burning fuels.
3) It will decrease.
4) endothermic
5) The overall energy change/the energy given out in the reaction.

Exam Questions

1 thermal decomposition *[1 mark]*
2.1 E.g. to ensure that they are the same temperature before beginning the reaction/ to know their initial temperature *[1 mark]*.
2.2 E.g. to insulate the cup/reduce the amount of heat lost to the surroundings *[1 mark]*.
2.3 The student should repeat the experiment under the same conditions *[1 mark]*. The measurement is repeatable if the student obtains similar results in both repeats *[1 mark]*.
3 C *[1 mark]*

Topic 6 — The Rate and Extent of Chemical Change

Page 96
Warm-Up Questions

1) E.g. the rusting of iron is a reaction that happens very slowly. Burning/combustion is a very fast reaction.
2) They must collide with enough energy / the activation energy.
3) Breaking a reactant into smaller pieces increases its surface area to volume ratio. This means there is a greater surface area available for collisions to occur on, so the rate of reaction is increased.
4) True

Exam Questions

1.1 The rate would increase *[1 mark]*.
1.2 The rate would increase *[1 mark]*.
2.1 A *[1 mark]*
2.2 C *[1 mark]*
2.3 Increasing the temperature means that the reactant particles move faster *[1 mark]*, so collisions between reactant particles are more frequent *[1 mark]*. The particles also have more energy *[1 mark]*, so more collisions have enough energy to make the reaction happen *[1 mark]*.
3.1

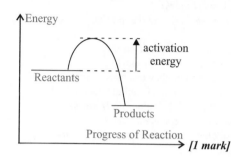

[1 mark]

3.2

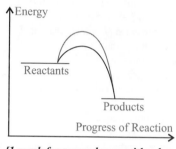

[1 mark for curve drawn with a lower maximum]

Pages 104-105
Warm-Up Questions

1) e.g. a mass balance / gas syringe / stopwatch / timer
2) Reaction A
3) False
A steep tangent on a rate graph means that the rate of reaction is fast at that point in time.
4) The backwards reaction

Exam Questions

1.1 The reaction is reversible *[1 mark]*.
1.2 As A and B react, their concentrations will **fall** *[1 mark]* and the rate of the forwards reaction will decrease. As C and D are made, the **backwards** *[1 mark]* reaction speeds up. After a while, the amounts of products and reactants will remain **constant** *[1 mark]*. The system is at equilibrium.
2.1 stopwatch/stopclock/timer *[1 mark]*
2.2 gas syringe *[1 mark]*
2.3 E.g. mass balances are very accurate / give very accurate results *[1 mark]*.
2.4 E.g. potentially harmful gases are released into the room *[1 mark]*.
3.1 17 cm^3 *[1 mark]*
3.2 Manganese(IV) oxide was the most effective catalyst *[1 mark]* because it led to the greatest volume of oxygen being produced over the time period measured/increased the rate of reaction by the greatest amount *[1 mark]*.
3.3 Draw tangents to each of the curves at 2 minutes *[1 mark]*, and compare how steep they are *[1 mark]*. A steeper tangent means a faster rate (and vice versa) *[1 mark]*.

4 How to grade your answer:
Level 0: There is no relevant information. *[No marks]*
Level 1: Simple statements are made which demonstrate some understanding of how colour change or the formation of a precipitate can be used to investigate the rate of reaction. The response lacks detail or logical structure. *[1 to 2 marks]*
Level 2: The method is described in relevant detail and demonstrates a broad understanding of how colour change or the formation of a precipitate can be used to investigate the rate of reaction. The answer follows a logical structure. *[3 to 4 marks]*
Here are some points your answer may include:
Add one of the reactants to a conical flask.
Place the conical flask over a black mark or cross that can be seen through the solution.
Add the second reactant to the conical flask.
The solution will turn cloudy.
Use a stopwatch to measure the time taken for the mark to disappear.
The faster the mark disappears, the faster the rate of reaction.
Repeat the experiment using different concentrations of reactant Y.
All other variables must be kept constant.
5.1 mean rate of reaction = amount of product formed ÷ time
mean rate of reaction = 46 ÷ 250 = **0.18 cm^3/s**
[3 marks for a rate between 0.17 cm^3/s and 0.19 cm^3/s, otherwise 1 mark for correct working and 1 mark for correct units]
Remember that the reaction is complete at the point where the line goes flat, so the total reaction time is 250 seconds.
5.2 mean rate of reaction = amount of product formed ÷ time
mean rate of reaction = (44 − 29) ÷ (150 − 40) = 15 ÷ 110
mean rate of reaction = 0.1363... = **0.14 cm^3/s**
[3 marks for correct answer, otherwise 1 mark for calculating change in x (110) and 1 mark for calculating change in y (15)]

Topic 7 — Organic Chemistry

Page 113-114
Warm-Up Questions

1) methane, ethane, propane, butane
2) (single) covalent bonds
3) They release lots of energy when burnt.
5) long-chain/large hydrocarbons

Exam Questions

1 ethane *[1 mark]*
2 Flammability decreases and viscosity increases. *[1 mark]*
3.1 butane *[1 mark]*
3.2 C_4H_{10} *[1 mark]*
3.3 Any two from: e.g. polymers / solvents / lubricants / detergents *[2 marks — 1 mark for each correct answer]*
4 Oxygen reacts with a fuel and energy is released. *[1 mark]*
5.1 $C_9H_{20} \rightarrow C_7H_{16} + C_2H_4$ *[1 mark]*
5.2 When bromine water is shaken with heptane, it remains orange in colour *[1 mark]*. When bromine water is shaken with ethene, it turns from orange to colourless *[1 mark]*.
Ethene is an alkene, so it turns bromine water colourless. Heptane is an alkane, so it doesn't react with bromine water.

6.1   A *[1 mark]*

6.2   Hydrocarbons with longer chains have higher boiling points *[1 mark]*. The column is hot at the bottom and gets cooler as you go up *[1 mark]*. The longer hydrocarbons condense back to liquids and drain out of the column at the higher temperatures lower down *[1 mark]*.

Topic 8 — Chemical Analysis

Pages 122-123
Warm-Up Questions

1)   Impurities in a substance will increase the boiling point of the substance and may also cause the substance to boil across a range of temperatures.

2)   e.g. paint/cleaning products/fuels/medicines/ cosmetics/fertilisers/metal alloys/food/drink

3)   Chromatography separates out the substances present in a mixture.

4)   False

An R_f value represents the ratio between the distance travelled by a dissolved substance and the distance travelled by the solvent.

Exam Questions

1

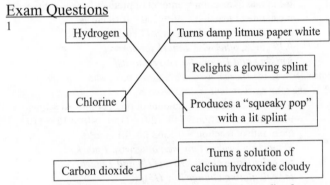

[3 marks — 1 mark for each correctly drawn line.]

2   Substance B only *[1 mark]*

Impurities lower the melting point of a substance, and may cause the sample to melt across a range of temperatures. Substance B is the only substance in the table that has an experimental melting point that is exactly the same as the data book value, so it is the only pure substance.

3   The brown group *[1 mark]*

4.1   B *[1 mark]*

4.2   C *[1 mark]*

4.3 R_f = distance moved by substance ÷ distance moved by solvent

        R_f = 9.0 ÷ 12.0 = **0.75**

        [2 marks for correct answer, otherwise 1 mark for correctly substituting the values into the formula for R_f.]

Topic 9 — Chemistry of the Atmosphere

Pages 131-132
Warm-Up Questions

1)   Volcanoes

2)   e.g. limestone / coal

3)   e.g. coal / crude oil / natural gas

4)   True

5)   e.g. acid rain / respiratory problems

Exam Questions

1.1   When green plants first evolved, the Earth's early atmosphere was mostly **carbon dioxide** *[1 mark]* gas. These plants produced **oxygen** *[1 mark]* by the process of photosynthesis. Some of the **carbon** *[1 mark]* from dead plants eventually became 'locked up' in fossil fuels.

1.2 $6CO_2 + 6H_2O \rightarrow C_6H_{12}O_6 + 6O_2$
        [1 mark for both CO_2 and O_2 formulas correct, 1 mark for correct balancing of H_2O]

1.3   C *[1 mark]*

2.1   Natural gas *[1 mark]*

Natural gas, crude oil and coal are the three fossil fuels you need to know about.

2.2   combustion / oxidation *[1 mark]*

2.3   e.g. particulates / soot *[1 mark]*

2.4   E.g. if breathed in, they can cause respiratory problems. / They reflect sunlight back into space, causing global dimming *[2 marks — 1 mark for each correct description]*.

2.5   It doesn't have any colour or smell *[1 mark]*.

3.1   Methane *[1 mark]*

3.2   Greenhouse gases give out the thermal radiation in all directions *[1 mark]*, so some of the radiation is returned to earth *[1 mark]* where it warms the surface of the planet *[1 mark]*.

3.3   Any two from: e.g. deforestation / burning fossil fuels / agriculture / using landfill sites *[2 marks — 1 mark for each correct answer]*

3.4   E.g. rising sea levels / increased flooding / changes in rainfall / more frequent/severe storms / changes in temperature *[1 mark]*.

3.5   E.g. tax companies and individuals based on the amount of greenhouse gases they emit. / Put a limit on the emissions of all greenhouse gases a company can make. / Invest in research and technology to reduce emissions or capture greenhouse gases before they are released *[1 mark]*.

4   How to grade your answer:

     Level 0:   There is no relevant information. *[No marks]*

     Level 1:   There is a brief description of how carbon dioxide was removed from the atmosphere by the oceans, plants and algae, and/or how this led to the formation of coal. However some details are missing or incorrect and the answer lacks structure. *[1 to 2 marks]*

     Level 2:   There is a detailed description of how the oceans and plants and algae removed carbon dioxide from the atmosphere, and how this led to the formation of coal. The answer is clearly written and logically structured. *[3 to 4 marks]*

Here are some points your answer may include:

Carbon dioxide was removed from the atmosphere by dissolving in the oceans.

The dissolved carbon dioxide formed carbonates/sediments/ carbon-containing compounds in the ocean.

Green plants and algae took in carbon dioxide during photosynthesis

When marine plants and algae died, they were buried on the seabed.

Over a long time, the dead plants were squashed down, forming coal.

Topic 10 — Using Resources

Page 139
Warm-Up Questions
1) e.g. wool / rubber
2) True
3) Any two from: e.g. saves energy needed to make new metals / saves limited supplies of metals from the earth / cuts down on the amount of waste going to landfill.
4) To assess the effect a product would have on the environment over the course of its life.

Exam Questions
1.1 A natural resource that can be remade at least as fast as we use it *[1 mark]*.
1.2 E.g. reuse the cans / recycle the aluminium / use fewer cans *[1 mark]*.
2.1 How to grade your answer:
   Level 0: There is no relevant information. *[No marks]*
   Level 1: There is a brief discussion of some environmental impacts of each type of bag. The points made are basic, don't link together and don't cover all of the information given in Table 1. If a conclusion is present it may not link to the points made. *[1 to 2 marks]*
   Level 2: There is a logical discussion of possible environmental impacts of each type of bag, but there is limited detail. There is a good coverage of the information given in Table 1 and the answer has some structure. A clear conclusion is given. *[3 to 4 marks]*
   Level 3: There is a clear and detailed discussion of the possible environmental impacts of each type of bag. The answer has a logical structure and makes good use of the information given in Table 1. A conclusion is present that fits with the points given in the answer. *[5 to 6 marks]*
   Here are some points your answer may include:
   The raw materials used to make plastic bags come from crude oil, which is a non-renewable resource.
   Obtaining crude oil from the ground and processing it uses a lot of energy and results in air pollution due to the release of greenhouse gases.
   The raw materials used to make paper bags come from trees. Trees are a renewable resource, although they take up land that could be used for other uses e.g. growing crops.
   Cutting down trees and processing the raw timber requires energy.
   This energy is often generated by burning fossil fuels, which releases harmful greenhouse gases into the atmosphere.
   The manufacture of plastic bags involves many industrial processes (e.g. fractional distillation, cracking, polymerisation), which all require large amounts of energy.
   As this energy often comes from burning fossil fuels, the manufacture causes the release of pollution (e.g. greenhouse gases) into the atmosphere.
   The waste from the manufacturing of plastic bags can be used to make other products, which reduces the amount of waste being sent to landfill.

Manufacturing paper bags also requires lots of energy. This could come from burning fossil fuels and so would generate pollution, such as greenhouses gases, which have a negative impact on the environment.
The manufacture of paper bags also creates lots of waste, which has to be disposed of and may cause pollution (e.g. if sent to landfill).
Plastic bags are reusable, which could reduce the amount of waste sent to landfill.
Paper bags are usually not reusable, which could increase the amount of waste sent to landfill.
Plastic bags are not biodegradable so will stay in the environment for a long time if disposed of in landfill sites.
Plastic bags can release toxic substances into the ground and pollute the land.
Plastic bags that end up in the oceans can harm marine life and pollute the water.
Plastic bags can be recycled, which would reduce the need to extract raw materials to make new bags.
Paper bags are biodegradable so will break down more easily than plastic bags if sent to landfill sites, reducing the impact on the environment.
Paper bags are also non-toxic, so won't releases poisonous/ toxic substances into the environment after being disposed of.
Paper bags can be recycled, which would reduce the need to gather raw materials to make new bags.

2.2 E.g. some things can't be measured, so depend upon a person's own judgement *[1 mark]*. Companies might use selective LCAs to make their product look more environmentally-friendly for advertising purposes *[1 mark]*.

Pages 144-145
Warm-Up Questions
1) E.g. the levels of dissolved salts in the water aren't too high. / The water has a pH of between 6.5 and 8.5. / There aren't any bacteria or other microbes in the water.
2) True
3) effluent and sludge
4) True

Exam Questions
1.1 Screening *[1 mark]*
1.2 Bacteria *[1 mark]*
2.1 Water that is safe to drink *[1 mark]*.
2.2 To remove any solids from the water *[1 mark]*.
2.3 e.g. chlorine / ozone / ultraviolet light *[1 mark]*
3.1

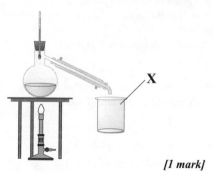

[1 mark]

3.2 When the water evaporates, it is separated from any soluble impurities, which are left in the flask *[1 mark]*. Condensation turns the steam back into liquid water, so it can be collected easily *[1 mark]*.

3.3 E.g. neutralise it / add acid until the pH is 7 *[1 mark]*.

3.4 All the seawater will have evaporated from the round bottomed flask *[1 mark]*.

3.5 The crystals are salts that were in the seawater before it was distilled *[1 mark]*.

The salts won't evaporate with the water, so they get left in the flask.

4.1 E.g. to remove any pollutants *[1 mark]* so that the water doesn't cause health problems / damage the environment *[1 mark]*.

Pollutants could be organic matter, bacteria and viruses etc.

4.2 Effluent is treated by aerobic digestion *[1 mark]* and sludge is treated by anaerobic digestion *[1 mark]*. In both processes, bacteria is used to break down the effluent/sludge *[1 mark]*.

4.3 E.g. it might contain harmful chemicals *[1 mark]*.

Industrial waste always needs further treatment before it is safe to return to the environment.

5.1 Seawater is passed through a membrane, which lets water molecules pass through *[1 mark]*, but traps the salts *[1 mark]*.

5.2 It requires a lot of energy *[1 mark]*.

Practice Paper 1

Pages 153-166

1.1 Neon *[1 mark]*

1.2 Metallic bonding *[1 mark]*

1.3 Copper *[1 mark]*

1.4 Fluorine *[1 mark]*

1.5 Protons = **9** *[1 mark]*
Neutrons = 19 − 9 = **10** *[1 mark]*
Electrons = **9** *[1 mark]*

Remember: number of protons = atomic number,
number of neutrons = mass number − atomic number,
number of electrons (in a neutral atom) = number of protons.

1.6 potassium chloride *[1 mark]*

1.7 Moving down Group 7, the outer electron shell gets further from the nucleus *[1 mark]*, and so it becomes harder for the halogens to gain an extra electron *[1 mark]*.

2.1 2560 − 1130 = 1430 g
= **1.43 × 10³ g**
[2 marks for correct answer given in standard form, otherwise 1 mark for correct answer not given in standard form.]

Remember, the total mass of the products must always be the same as the total mass of the reactants.

2.2 (aq): aqueous/dissolved in water *[1 mark]*
(s): solid *[1 mark]*

2.3 The reaction produces carbon dioxide gas *[1 mark]*. This escapes from the beaker, reducing the mass of the reaction mixture *[1 mark]*.

2.4 E.g.
224 cm³ ÷ 1000 = 0.224 dm³
3.4 g ÷ 0.224 dm³ = 15.17... g/dm³
= **15.2 g/dm³ (3 s.f.)**
[3 marks for correct answer given to 3 s.f. or 2 marks for correct answer not given to 3 s.f., otherwise 1 mark for converting from cm³ to dm³.]

Remember, to get from cm³ to dm³ you have to divide by 1000.

3.1 Two or more elements or compounds that are not chemically combined together / don't have any chemical bonds between them *[1 mark]*.

3.2 No chemical reactions take place during fractional distillation *[1 mark]*.

3.3 fractionating column *[1 mark]*

3.4 Compound: ethanoic acid *[1 mark]*
Reason: it has the highest boiling point *[1 mark]*.

3.5 78 °C *[1 mark]*

3.6 Any two from: e.g. wear gloves / wear a lab coat / wear goggles / work in a fume cupboard.
[2 marks — 1 mark for each sensible precaution.]

3.7 The boiling points of methanol and isobutanal are very similar *[1 mark]*.

4.1 E.g.

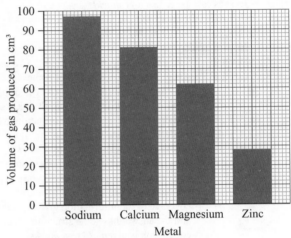

[1 mark for sensible scale on the vertical axis, 1 mark for all 4 bars plotted correctly]

Make sure any graphs you draw fill at least two-thirds of the space given.

4.2 hydrogen *[1 mark]*

4.3 e.g. 17 cm³ *[1 mark for answer in range 1-27 cm³.]*

To answer this question you need to remember than iron is below zinc in the reactivity series. This means it reacts more slowly with the acid, and so not as much gas is produced in 60 seconds.

4.4 $M_r = (2 × 23) + 32 + (4 × 16)$
$= 46 + 32 + 64$
$= \textbf{142}$ *[1 mark]*

4.5 percentage mass of an element in a compound
$= \dfrac{A_r × \text{number of atoms of that element}}{M_r \text{ of the compound}} × 100$
percentage mass of sodium $= \dfrac{23 × 2}{142} × 100$
$= 32.394...$
$= \textbf{32.4 (3 s.f.)}$
[2 marks for correct answer given to 3 s.f., otherwise 1 mark for correct answer not given to 3 s.f.]

You can still get the marks here if you got the wrong value for the M_r in 4.4 and used that in your calculation. Just make sure you did the right calculation and that your answer is correct for the value of M_r you used.

4.6 electrolyte *[1 mark]*

4.7 oxygen *[1 mark]*

There are no halide ions present in the solution, so it is OH⁻ ions from the water that lose electrons at the anode, forming O_2 (and H_2O).

4.8 Product at cathode: hydrogen *[1 mark]*
Reason: sodium is more reactive than hydrogen *[1 mark]*.

5.1   +1 *[1 mark]*

5.2   Any two from: e.g. potassium fizzes more than
sodium, which fizzes more than lithium. / Potassium
moves more quickly than sodium, which moves more
quickly than lithium. / Potassium appears to melt
and a flame is seen, sodium appears to melt but no
flame is seen and lithium does not appear to melt.
[2 marks — 1 mark for each correct observation]

5.3   As you go down Group 1 the outer electron gets further
from the nucleus *[1 mark]*. This means that the outer
electron is more easily lost because it is less attracted to the
nucleus *[1 mark]*. So reactivity increases as you go down
Group 1/from lithium to sodium to potassium *[1 mark]*.

5.4 $2K + 2H_2O \rightarrow 2KOH + H_2$ *[1 mark]*

5.5   It contains hydroxide ions *[1 mark]*.

5.6   2, 1 *[1 mark]*

6.1   Any two from: e.g. have a lid on the beaker. / Use insulation
(e.g. cotton wool) around the beaker. / Use a polystyrene
beaker. *[2 marks — 1 mark for each correct answer]*

6.2   temperature change *[1 mark]*

The dependent variable is the variable you measure.

6.3   1 °C *[1 mark]*

6.4   37.5 °C *[1 mark]*

6.5   Temperature change = final temperature – initial temperature
= 37.5 – 17 = **20.5 °C**
***[2 marks for correct answer, otherwise 1 mark for writing a
correct expression for calculating the temperature change.]***

*If your answer to 6.4 was wrong, you can still have both marks for correctly
subtracting 17 from it to find the temperature change.*

6.6   The reaction was exothermic as the temperature of the
surroundings increased during the reaction *[1 mark]*.

7.1   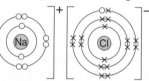

***[1 mark for adding seven crosses and one dot to outer
shell of Cl⁻ ion, 1 mark for correct charge on both ions.]***

7.2   63 °C *[1 mark]*

*Substance B is a gas at temperatures above its boiling point of –183 °C.
63 °C is the only temperature given which is higher than –183 °C, so
substance B must be a gas at this temperature.*

7.3   The molecules in substance A are only attracted to each
other by weak intermolecular forces *[1 mark]* which
don't need much energy to break/overcome *[1 mark]*.

7.4   Substance C *[1 mark]*. It can conduct electricity when
molten or dissolved but not when solid *[1 mark]*.

7.5   How to grade your answer:

Level 0:   There is no relevant information. *[No marks]*

Level 1:   A brief attempt is made to explain one or two
of these properties in terms of structure and
bonding. *[1-2 marks]*

Level 2:   Some explanation of two or three of the
properties, in terms of their structure and
bonding, is given. *[3-4 marks]*

Level 3:   Clear and detailed explanation of all three of
the properties, in terms of their structure and
bonding, is given. *[5-6 marks]*

Here are some points your answer may include:

Diamond

Each carbon atom in diamond forms four covalent bonds,
making it very hard.
Because it is made up of lots of covalent bonds, which take a
lot of energy to break, diamond has a very high melting point.
There are no free/delocalised electrons or ions in the
structure of diamond, so it can't conduct electricity.

Graphite

Each carbon atom in graphite forms three covalent bonds,
creating sheets of carbon atoms that can slide over each other.
The carbon layers are only held together weakly, which is
what makes graphite soft.
The covalent bonds between the carbon atoms take a lot of
energy to break, giving graphite a very high melting point.
Only three out of each carbon's four outer electrons are used
in bonds, so graphite has lots of free/delocalised electrons
which can conduct electricity.

Practice Paper 2

Pages 167-182

1.1   A resource that is used up more quickly
than it can be replaced *[1 mark]*.

1.2   Resource 3 *[1 mark]*

1.3   fractional distillation *[1 mark]*

1.4   Before it enters the column, the crude oil is heated until
it **evaporates** *[1 mark]*. Different hydrocarbons from
the crude oil then leave the column at different points
because they have different **boiling points** *[1 mark]*.

1.5   Petrol *[1 mark]*

1.6   Bitumen *[1 mark]*

1.7   Alkene *[1 mark]*

2.1   It is the mobile phase *[1 mark]*

2.2   So the spots of food colouring do not dissolve
into the solvent in the beaker *[1 mark]*.

2.3   The student could get another person to do the
chromatography experiment too, using the same
method and conditions *[1 mark]*, and check that the
results from both experiments are similar *[1 mark]*.

2.4   The unknown food colouring is most likely to be pure, as it
has only formed one spot on the chromatogram *[1 mark]*.

2.5   three *[1 mark]*

2.6   E.g.
distance moved by spot **Y** from the baseline = 1.9 cm
distance moved by solvent from the baseline = 4.1 cm
R_f = 1.9 ÷ 4.1
= 0.4634...
= **0.46 (2 s.f.)**
*[5 marks for correct answer in range 0.43-0.50 given to
2 s.f. or 4 marks for correct answer in range 0.43-0.50
not given to 2 s.f., otherwise 1 mark for distance moved
by spot Y in range 1.8-2.0 cm, 1 mark for distance moved
by solvent in range 4.0-4.2 cm, 1 mark for correctly
substituting values into equation.]*

2.7   The student's sample is not pure, as its melting point is
lower than the data book value for the melting point of the
substance *[1 mark]*.

3.1   The concentration of carbon dioxide in the atmosphere has
increased over time *[1 mark]*. It stayed roughly the same
for the first 75 years before increasing slowly from 1775,
then increasingly more rapidly after 1900 *[1 mark]*.

3.2   It has been peer-reviewed *[1 mark]*.

3.3   Greenhouse effect *[1 mark]*

3.4   How to grade your answer:

Level 0:   There is no relevant information. *[No marks]*

Level 1:   There are some correct and relevant points, but no overall comparison of the environmental impacts. *[1-2 marks]*

Level 2:   A range of correct and relevant points are made, leading to an overall comparison of the environmental impacts. *[3-4 marks]*

Here are some points your answer may include:

Less carbon dioxide is given out manufacturing a plastic bottle than manufacturing a glass bottle.

Transporting plastic bottles produces less carbon dioxide than transporting glass bottles (as they are lighter).

Glass bottles are made mostly from recycled glass.

Plastic bottles are usually produced from new raw materials, using up more crude oil.

More glass bottles than plastic bottles get recycled.

More carbon dioxide is given out manufacturing and transporting glass bottles than plastic bottles, but less waste is produced/less new raw materials are needed as glass bottles are easier to recycle.

Less carbon dioxide is given out manufacturing and transporting plastic bottles than glass bottles, but more waste is produced/more raw materials are needed as plastic bottles are harder to recycle.

4.1   surface area of the calcium carbonate *[1 mark]*
temperature *[1 mark]*

4.2   Bubbling the gas through a solution of calcium hydroxide *[1 mark]*.

4.3   Volume of gas produced after 30 seconds in Experiment 1
= **86-88 cm³** *[1 mark]*
Volume of gas produced after 30 seconds in Experiment 2
= **139-141 cm³** *[1 mark]*

You get the marks for any answer within each range.

4.4   E.g. the curve for Experiment 2 starts off steeper than the curve for Experiment 1. / The curve for Experiment 2 flattens out more quickly than the curve for Experiment 1, with the same total amount of gas produced *[1 mark]*.

4.5   Increasing the concentration increases the number of particles in the reaction mixture *[1 mark]*. This increases the frequency of collisions *[1 mark]*.

4.6   mass of calcium sulfate formed = mass of weighing boat with calcium sulfate – mass of weighing boat
mass of calcium sulfate formed = 2.22 – 1.36
= **0.86 g** *[1 mark]*

4.7   From the graph, the reaction finished after 55 seconds.
So time taken = 55 seconds
mean rate of reaction = 0.86 ÷ 55
= 0.01563...
= **0.016 g/s (2.s.f.)**

[3 marks for correct answer in range of 0.014-0.016, given to 2 s.f. or 2 marks for correct answer in range of 0.014-0.016 not given to 2 s.f., otherwise 1 mark for time of 55-60 seconds taken from graph]

5.1 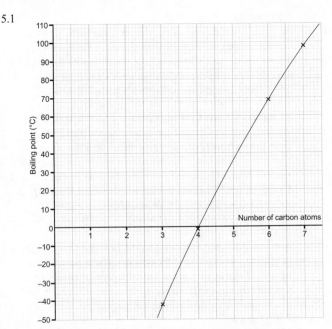

[1 mark for all four points correctly plotted, 1 mark for a smooth curve that passes through all the points]

5.2   E.g. 36 °C
[1 mark for correct reading of the graph drawn in 5.1]

Even if the graph you drew in question 5.1. was wrong, if you've used it correctly to find a value for the boiling point of a molecule with 5 carbon atoms, you get the mark here.

5.3 C_nH_{2n+2} *[1 mark]*

5.4
$$H-\overset{\displaystyle H}{\underset{\displaystyle H}{C}}-\overset{\displaystyle H}{\underset{\displaystyle H}{C}}-\overset{\displaystyle H}{\underset{\displaystyle H}{C}}-H$$
[1 mark]

5.5   Add a few drops of bromine water to both compounds and shake *[1 mark]*. With propane, nothing will happen *[1 mark]*. Propene will decolourise the bromine water / turn the solution from orange to colourless *[1 mark]*.

5.6 $C_3H_8 + 5O_2 \rightarrow 3CO_2 +$ **$4H_2O$**
[1 mark for correctly giving H_2O as the missing product, 1 mark for correct number in front of H_2O.]

5.7   Heptane has a higher viscosity than propane *[1 mark]*, as its molecular formula shows that it has more atoms in its carbon chain/has a longer carbon chain/is a bigger molecule *[1 mark]*.

6.1   As the level of nitrogen dioxide increases, the severity of asthma attacks increases / there is a positive correlation between the nitrogen dioxide level and severity of asthma attacks *[1 mark]*

6.2   E.g. the scientists only collected data from men. / The scientists only collected data from people under 40. / The severity of asthma attacks might be affected by another pollutant which happens to be abundant in the same areas as nitrogen dioxide. *[1 mark]*

6.3   Oxides of nitrogen are formed when nitrogen and oxygen from the air react at high temperatures *[1 mark]*. This happens when fuel is burned in car engines *[1 mark]*. In cities, there are lots of cars, so the levels of nitrogen oxides tend to be higher *[1 mark]*.

6.4   Cool the reaction mixture. / Reduce the temperature the reaction is carried out at *[1 mark]*.

6.5   E.g. sulfur dioxide *[1 mark]*

7.1 E.g. they don't have enough fresh water / groundwater / surface water to treat and use as drinking water *[1 mark]*.

7.2 Desalination *[1 mark]*

7.3 How to grade your answer:

Level 0: There is no relevant information. *[No marks]*

Level 1: There is a brief description of the method to distil seawater, but many details are missing or incorrect. *[1 to 2 marks]*

Level 2: There is some explanation of the method used to distil sea water. Most of the information is correct, but a few small details may be incorrect or missing. *[3 to 4 marks]*

Level 3: There is a clear, detailed and fully correct explanation of the method used to distil sea water in the lab. *[5 to 6 marks]*

Here are some points your answer may include:

Pour the sea water into a (round bottom) flask.

Attach the flask to a condenser and secure both with clamps.

Connect a supply of cold water to the condenser.

Place a beaker under the condenser to collect the fresh water.

Place a Bunsen burner under the round bottom flask and heat the sea water slowly.

The water will boil and form steam.

The steam will condense back to pure liquid water in the condenser and be collected in the beaker as it runs out.

Continue to heat the (round bottom) flask until all the water has evaporated.

7.4 Large bits of material (such as grit) are removed from the sewage *[1 mark]*.

7.5 The effluent undergoes aerobic biological treatment *[1 mark]*. Aerobic bacteria break down any organic matter that is present *[1 mark]*.

Index

Index

The Periodic Table

	Hydrogen
1	H
	1

Relative atomic mass

Atomic (proton) number

Halogens

Noble gases / *going up*

good conductors

Transition metals

Alkali metals

Reactive

Periods	Group 1	Group 2												Group 3	Group 4	Group 5	Group 6	Group 7	Group 0
1																			4 He Helium 2
2	7 Li Lithium 3	9 Be Beryllium 4												11 B Boron 5	12 C Carbon 6	14 N Nitrogen 7	16 O Oxygen 8	19 F Fluorine 9	20 Ne Neon 10
3	23 Na Sodium 11	24 Mg Magnesium 12												27 Al Aluminium 13	28 Si Silicon 14	31 P Phosphorus 15	32 S Sulfur 16	35.5 Cl Chlorine 17	40 Ar Argon 18
4	39 K Potassium 19	40 Ca Calcium 20	45 Sc Scandium 21	48 Ti Titanium 22	51 V Vanadium 23	52 Cr Chromium 24	55 Mn Manganese 25	56 Fe Iron 26	59 Co Cobalt 27	59 Ni Nickel 28	63.5 Cu Copper 29	65 Zn Zinc 30		70 Ga Gallium 31	73 Ge Germanium 32	75 As Arsenic 33	79 Se Selenium 34	80 Br Bromine 35	84 Kr Krypton 36
5	85 Rb Rubidium 37	88 Sr Strontium 38	89 Y Yttrium 39	91 Zr Zirconium 40	93 Nb Niobium 41	96 Mo Molybdenum 42	[98] Tc Technetium 43	101 Ru Ruthenium 44	103 Rh Rhodium 45	106 Pd Palladium 46	108 Ag Silver 47	112 Cd Cadmium 48		115 In Indium 49	119 Sn Tin 50	122 Sb Antimony 51	128 Te Tellurium 52	127 I Iodine 53	131 Xe Xenon 54
6	133 Cs Caesium 55	137 Ba Barium 56	139 La Lanthanum 57	178 Hf Hafnium 72	181 Ta Tantalum 73	184 W Tungsten 74	186 Re Rhenium 75	190 Os Osmium 76	192 Ir Iridium 77	195 Pt Platinum 78	197 Au Gold 79	201 Hg Mercury 80		204 Tl Thallium 81	207 Pb Lead 82	209 Bi Bismuth 83	[209] Po Polonium 84	[210] At Astatine 85	[222] Rn Radon 86
7	[223] Fr Francium 87	[226] Ra Radium 88	[227] Ac Actinium 89	[261] Rf Rutherfordium 104	[262] Db Dubnium 105	[266] Sg Seaborgium 106	[264] Bh Bohrium 107	[277] Hs Hassium 108	[268] Mt Meitnerium 109	[271] Ds Darmstadtium 110	[272] Rg Roentgenium 111	[285] Cn Copernicium 112		[286] Nh Nihonium 113	[289] Fl Flerovium 114	[289] Mc Moscovium 115	[293] Lv Livermorium 116	[294] Ts Tennessine 117	[294] Og Oganesson 118

The Lanthanides (atomic numbers 58-71) and the Actinides (atomic numbers 90-103) are not shown in this table.